D1473341

Project-Based Inquiry Science™

ASTRONOMY

Janet L. Kolodner

Joseph S. Krajcik

Daniel C. Edelson

Brian J. Reiser

Mary L. Starr

NSF

IT'S ABOUT TIME®

YOUR PARTNER IN STEM EDUCATION

IT'S ABOUT TIME®

YOUR PARTNER IN STEM EDUCATION

333 North Bedford Road, Mount Kisco, NY 10549
Phone (914) 273-2233 Fax (914) 206-6444
www.IAT.com

Program Components

Student Edition   Durable Equipment Kit

Teacher's Planning Guide   Consumable Equipment Kit

                                    Multimedia

                                    — PBIS Content DVD

ISBN 978-1-60720-795-5

3rd Printing

3 4 5 6   17 16 15 14

This project was supported, in part, by the **National Science Foundation**
under grant nos. 0137807, 0527341, and 0639978.
Opinions expressed are those of the authors and not necessarily
those of the National Science Foundation.

Principal Investigators

Janet L. Kolodner is a Regents' Professor in the School of Interactive Computing in the Georgia Institute of Technology's College of Computing. Since 1978, her research has focused on learning from experience, both in computers and in people. She pioneered the Artificial Intelligence method called *case-based reasoning*, providing a way for computers to solve new problems based on their past experiences. Her book, *Case-Based Reasoning*, synthesizes work across the case-based reasoning research community from its inception to 1993.

Since 1994, Dr. Kolodner has focused on the applications and implications of case-based reasoning for education. In her approach to science education, called Learning by Design™ (LBD), students learn science while pursuing design challenges. Dr. Kolodner has investigated how to create a culture of collaboration and rigorous science talk in classrooms, how to use a project challenge to promote focus on science content, and how students learn and develop when classrooms function as learning communities. Currently, Dr. Kolodner is investigating how to help young people come to think of themselves as scientific reasoners. Dr. Kolodner's research results have been widely published, including in *Cognitive Science, Design Studies,* and the *Journal of the Learning Sciences.*

Dr. Kolodner was founding Director of Georgia Tech's EduTech Institute, served as coordinator of Georgia Tech's Cognitive Science program for many years, and is founding Editor in Chief of the *Journal of the Learning Sciences*. She is a founder of the International Society for the Learning Sciences, and she served as its first Executive Officer. She is a fellow of the American Association of Artificial Intelligence.

Joseph S. Krajcik is a Professor of Science Education and Associate Dean for Research in the School of Education at the University of Michigan. He works with teachers in science classrooms to bring about sustained change by creating classroom environments in which students find solutions to important intellectual questions that subsume essential curriculum standards and use learning technologies as productivity tools. He seeks to discover what students learn in such environments, as well as to explore and find solutions to challenges that teachers face in enacting such complex instruction. Dr. Krajcik has authored and co-authored over 100 manuscripts and makes frequent presentations at international, national, and regional conferences that focus on his research, as well as presentations that translate research findings into classroom practice. He is a fellow of the American Association for the Advancement of Science and served as president of the National Association for Research in Science Teaching. Dr. Krajcik co-directs the Center for Highly Interactive Classrooms, Curriculum and Computing in Education at the University of Michigan and is a co-principal investigator in the Center for Curriculum Materials in Science and The National Center for Learning and Teaching Nanoscale Science and Engineering. In 2002, Dr. Krajcik was honored to receive a Guest Professorship from Beijing Normal University in Beijing, China. In winter 2005, he was the Weston Visiting Professor of Science Education at the Weizmann Institute of Science in Rehovot, Israel.

 **Daniel C. Edelson** has been engaged in research and development in geosciences and geography education since 1992. From 1994-2007, he was a faculty member in the School of Education and Social Policy at Northwestern University, where he founded and led the Geographic Data in Education (GEODE) Initiative. In addition to his work on *Planetary Forecaster* and *Ever-Changing Earth* for PBIS, Dr. Edelson is the author of a high-school environmental science text, *Investigations in Environmental Science: A Case-Based Approach to the Study of Environmental Systems,* and of *My World GIS™*, a geographic information system for inquiry-based learning. His research on science education and educational technology has been widely published, including articles in the *Journal of the Learning Sciences, the Journal of Research on Science Teaching, Science Educator,* and *The Science Teacher.*

 **Brian J. Reiser** is a Professor of Learning Sciences in the School of Education and Social Policy at Northwestern University. Professor Reiser served as chair of Northwestern's Learning Sciences Ph.D. program from 1993, shortly after its inception, until 2001. His research focuses on the design and enactment of learning environments that support students' inquiry in science, including both science curriculum materials and scaffolded software tools. His research investigates the design of learning environments that scaffold scientific practices, including investigation, argumentation, and explanation; design principles for technology-infused curricula that engage students in inquiry projects; and the teaching practices that support student inquiry. Professor Reiser also directed BGuILE (Biology Guided Inquiry Learning Environments) to develop software tools for supporting middle school and high school students in analyzing data and constructing explanations with biological data. Reiser is a co-principal investigator in the NSF Center for Curriculum Materials in Science. He served as a member of the NRC panel authoring the report Taking Science to School.

 **Mary L. Starr** is a Research Specialist in Science Education in the School of Education at the University of Michigan. She collaborates with teachers and students in elementary and middle school science classrooms around the United States who are implementing *Project-Based Inquiry Science*. Before joining the PBIS team, Dr. Starr created professional learning experiences in science, math, and technology, designed to assist teachers in successfully changing their classroom practices to promote student learning from coherent inquiry experiences. She has developed instructional materials in several STEM areas, including nanoscale science education, has presented at national and regional teacher education and educational research meetings, and has served in a leadership role in the Michigan Science Education Leadership Association. Dr. Starr has authored articles and book chapters, and has worked to improve elementary science teacher preparation through teaching science courses for pre-service teachers and acting as a consultant in elementary science teacher preparation. As part of the PBIS team, Dr. Starr has played a lead role in making units cohere as a curriculum, in developing the framework for PBIS Teacher's Planning Guides, and in developing teacher professional development experiences and materials.

Acknowledgements

Three research teams contributed to the development of *Project-Based Inquiry Science (PBIS)*: a team at the Georgia Institute of Technology headed by Janet L. Kolodner, a team at Northwestern University headed by Daniel Edelson and Brian Reiser, and a team at the University of Michigan headed by Joseph Krajcik and Ron Marx. Each of the PBIS units was originally developed by one of these teams and then later revised and edited to be a part of the full three-year middle-school curriculum that became PBIS.

PBIS has its roots in two educational approaches, Project-Based Science and Learning by Design™. Project-Based Science suggests that students should learn science through engaging in the same kinds of inquiry practices scientists use, in the context of scientific problems relevant to their lives and using tools authentic to science. Project-Based Science was originally conceived in the hi-ce Center at the University of Michigan, with funding from the National Science Foundation. Learning by Design™ derives from Problem-Based Learning and suggests sequencing, social practices, and reflective activities for promoting learning. It engages students in design practices, including the use of iteration and deliberate reflection. LBD was conceived at the Georgia Institute of Technology, with funding from the National Science Foundation, DARPA, and the McDonnell Foundation.

The development of the integrated *PBIS* curriculum was supported by the National Science Foundation under grant nos. 0137807, 0527341, and 0639978. Any opinions, findings and conclusions, or recommendations expressed in this material are those of the authors and do not necessarily reflect the views of the National Science Foundation.

PBIS Team

Principal Investigator
Janet L. Kolodner

Co-Principal Investigators
Daniel C. Edelson
Joseph S. Krajcik
Brian J. Reiser

NSF Program Officer
Gerhard Salinger

Curriculum Developers
Michael T. Ryan
Mary L. Starr

Teacher's Planning Guide Developers
Rebecca M. Schneider
Mary L. Starr

Literacy Specialist
LeeAnn M. Sutherland

NSF Program Reviewer
Arthur Eisenkraft

Project Coordinator
Juliana Lancaster

External Evaluators
The Learning Partnership
Steven M. McGee
Jennifer Witers

The Georgia Institute of Technology Team

Project Director:
Janet L. Kolodner

Development of PBIS units at the Georgia Institute of Technology was conducted in conjunction with the Learning by Design™ Research group (LBD), Janet L. Kolodner, PI.

Lead Developers, Physical Science:
David Crismond
Michael T. Ryan

Lead Developer, Earth Science:
Paul J. Camp

Assessment and Evaluation:
Barbara Fasse
Jackie Gray
Daniel Hickey
Jennifer Holbrook
Laura Vandewiele

Project Pioneers:
JoAnne Collins
David Crismond
Joanna Fox
Alice Gertzman
Mark Guzdial
Cindy Hmelo-Silver
Douglas Holton
Roland Hubscher
N. Hari Narayanan
Wendy Newstetter
Valery Petrushin
Kathy Politis
Sadhana Puntambekar
David Rector
Janice Young

The Northwestern University Team

Project Directors:
Daniel Edelson
Brian Reiser

Lead Developer, Biology:
David Kanter

Lead Developers, Earth Science:
Jennifer Mundt Leimberer
Darlene Slusher

Development of PBIS units at Northwestern was conducted in conjunction with:

The Center for Learning Technologies in Urban Schools (LeTUS) at Northwestern, and the Chicago Public Schools
Clifton Burgess, PI
for Chicago Public Schools;
Louis Gomez, PI.

The BioQ Collaborative
David Kanter, PI.

The Biology Guided Inquiry Learning Environments (BGuILE) Project
Brian Reiser, PI.

The Geographic Data in Education (GEODE) Initiative
Daniel Edelson, Director

The Center for Curriculum Materials in Science at Northwestern
Daniel Edelson,
Brian Reiser,
Bruce Sherin, PIs.

The University of Michigan Team

Project Directors:
Joseph Krajcik
Ron Marx

Literacy Specialist:
LeeAnn M. Sutherland

Project Coordinator:
Mary L. Starr

Development of PBIS units at the University of Michigan was conducted in conjunction with:

The Center for Learning Technologies in Urban Schools (LeTUS)
Phyllis Blumenfeld,
Barry Fishman,
Joseph Krajcik,
Ron Marx,
Elliot Soloway, PIs.

The Detroit Public Schools
Juanita Clay-Chambers
Deborah Peek-Brown

The Center for Highly Interactive Computing in Education (hi-ce)
Phyllis Blumenfeld,
Barry Fishman,
Joseph Krajcik,
Ron Marx,
Elizabeth Moje,
Elliot Soloway,
LeeAnn Sutherland, PIs.

Field-Test Teachers

National Field Test
Tamica Andrew
Leslie Baker
Jeanne Bayer
Gretchen Bryant
Boris Consuegra
Daun D'Aversa
Candi DiMauro
Kristie L. Divinski
Donna M. Dowd
Jason Fiorito
Lara Fish
Christine Gleason
Christine Hallerman
Terri L. Hart-Parker
Jennifer Hunn
Rhonda K. Hunter
Jessica Jones
Dawn Kuppersmith
Anthony F. Lawrence
Ann Novak
Rise Orsini
Tracy E. Parham
Cheryl Sgro-Ellis
Debra Tenenbaum
Sarah B. Topper
Becky Watts
Debra A. Williams
Ingrid M. Woolfolk
Ping-Jade Yang

New York City Field Test
Several sequences of PBIS units have been field-tested in New York City under the leadership of Whitney Lukens, Staff Developer for Region 9, and Greg Borman, Science Instructional Specialist, New York City Department of Education

6th Grade
Norman Agard
Tazinmudin Ali
Heather
   Guthartz Aniba
Asher Arzonane
Asli Aydin
Shareese Blakely
John J. Blaylock
Joshua Blum
Tsedey Bogale

Filomena Borrero
Zachary Brachio
Thelma Brown
Alicia Browne-Jones
Scott Bullis
Maximo Cabral
Lionel Callender
Matthew Carpenter
Ana Maria Castro
Diane Castro
Anne Chan
Ligia Chiorean
Boris Consuegra
Careen Halton Cooper
Cinnamon Czarnecki
Kristin Decker
Nancy Dejean
Gina DiCicco
Donna Dowd
Lizanne Espina
Joan Ferrato
Matt Finnerty
Jacqueline Flicker
Helen Fludd
Leigh Summers Frey
Helene Friedman-Hager
Diana Gering
Matthew Giles
Lucy Gill
Steven Gladden
Greg Grambo
Carrie Grodin-Vehling
Stephan Joanides
Kathryn Kadei
Paraskevi Karangunis
Cynthia Kerns
Martine Lalanne
Erin Lalor
Jennifer Lerman
Sara Lugert
Whitney Lukens
Dana Martorella
Christine Mazurek
Janine McGeown
Chevelle McKeever
Kevin Meyer
Jennifer Miller
Nicholas Miller
Diana Neligan
Caitlin Van Ness
Marlyn Orque
Eloisa Gelo Ortiz
Gina Papadopoulos
Tim Perez
Albertha Petrochilos
Christopher Poli

Kristina Rodriguez
Nadiesta Sanchez
Annette Schavez
Hilary Sedgwitch
Elissa Seto
Laura Shectman
Audrey Shmuel
Katherine Silva
Ragini Singhal
C. Nicole Smith
Gitangali Sohit
Justin Stein
Thomas Tapia
Eilish Walsh-Lennon
Lisa Wong
Brian Yanek
Cesar Yarleque
David Zaretsky
Colleen Zarinsky

7th Grade
Mayra Amaro
Emmanuel Anastasiou
Cheryl Barnhill
Bryce Cahn
Ligia Chiorean
Ben Colella
Boris Consuegra
Careen Halton Cooper
Elizabeth Derse
Urmilla Dhanraj
Gina DiCicco
Lydia Doubleday
Lizanne Espina
Matt Finnerty
Steven Gladden
Stephanie Goldberg
Nicholas Graham
Robert Hunter
Charlene Joseph
Ketlynne Joseph
Kimberly Kavazanjian
Christine Kennedy
Bakwah Kotung
Lisa Kraker
Anthony Lett
Herb Lippe
Jennifer Lopez
Jill Mastromarino
Kerry McKie
Christie Morgado
Patrick O'Connor
Agnes Ochiagha
Tim Perez
Nadia Piltser
Chris Poli

Carmelo Ruiz
Kim Sanders
Leslie Schiavone
Ileana Solla
Jacqueline Taylor
Purvi Vora
Ester Wiltz
Carla Yuille
Marcy Sexauer Zacchea
Lidan Zhou

8th Grade
Emmanuel Anastasio
Jennifer Applebaum
Marsha Armstrong
Jenine Barunas
Vito Cipolla
Kathy Critharis
Patrecia Davis
Alison Earle
Lizanne Espina
Matt Finnerty
Ursula Fokine
Kirsis Genao
Steven Gladden
Stephanie Goldberg
Peter Gooding
Matthew Herschfeld
Mike Horowitz
Charlene Jenkins
Ruben Jimenez
Ketlynne Joseph
Kimberly Kavazanjian
Lisa Kraker
Dora Kravitz
Anthony Lett
Emilie Lubis
George McCarthy
David Mckinney
Michael McMahon
Paul Melhado
Jen Miller
Christie Morgado
Maria Jenny Pineda
Anastasia Plaunova
Carmelo Ruiz
Riza Sanchez
Kim Sanders
Maureen Stefanides
Dave Thompson
Matthew Ulmann
Maria Verosa
Tony Yaskulski

Astronomy

Astronomy (PBIS) is based on *Astronomy*, a unit developed by the University of Michigan's Center for Highly Interactive Computing in Education (hi ce).

Astronomy (PBIS version)
Lead Developer
Mary L. Starr

Contributor
Julia Plummer
Deano Smith

Astronomy (Michigan version)
Lead Developer
Julia Plummer
Other Developer
Mary Pat Pardo
Other Contributors
Lisa Scott Holt
Steve Best
Joe Krajcik
Matthew P. Linke

The development of all versions of *Astronomy* was supported by the National Science Foundation under grant nos. 0137807, 0527341, and 0639978. Any opinions, findings, and conclusions or recommendations expressed in this material are those of the authors and do not necessarily reflect the views of the National Science Foundation.

Table of Contents

What's the Big Question?

Learning Set 1

Science Concepts: *Historical contributions in astronomy, impact craters, telescopes, characteristics of impact craters, satellite images, astrogeology, erosion and weathering, age of geological features (Earth and the Moon), meteors and meteorites, components of the solar system, asteroids, comets, asteroid belt, designing an experiment, understanding models, independent and dependent variables, experimental controls, making predictions, communicating plans, analyzing data, working with maps, using visualization tools, using evidence to support claims, developing explanations.*

Learning Set 2

Science Concepts: *Apparent motion, rotation and revolution, definition of a day, the Sun as the source of reflected light, phases of the Moon, orbital motion, Earth-Moon-Sun system, relative sizes of objects in the solar system, measurement on the celestial sphere, lunar eclipses and solar eclipses, total eclipses and partial eclipses, shadows (umbra and penumbra), characteristics of the Sun, solar atmosphere, fusion in stars, sunspots, gravity and motion, tides, formation of the Moon, understanding models, collecting and organizing data, building models, developing explanations, using evidence to support claims, using scientific knowledge, using visualization tools, simulations, scale models, scientific theories, making measurements.*

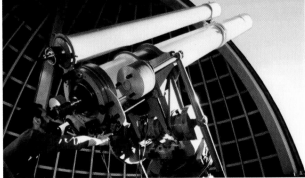

Learning Set 3

Science Concepts: *Position of objects in the solar system, distances between solar system objects, scale models, calculating scale factors, designing models of the solar system, comparing characteristics of planets (inner and outer planets), revolution and definition of a year, astronomical unit, gravity and planetary motion, orbital characteristics, apparent motion of planets, heliocentric and geocentric models of the solar system, historical contributions in astronomy, formation of the solar system, using visualization tools, understanding models, building models, collaboration, building on the work of others, organizing and analyzing data, finding trends in data, using evidence to support claims.*

Learning Set 4

Science Concepts: *Space exploration, telescopes, photography and astronomy, stellar magnitude, distance measurement in astronomy (parallax and indirect methods), astronomical units of distance, characteristics of the Milky Way galaxy, the Sun's position in the Milky Way galaxy, stellar spectra, Doppler shifts, historical contributions in astronomy, classification of stars, types of stars (main sequence, giant, supergiant, white dwarf, neutron star), radio astronomy, black holes, stellar evolution, nebulae and the formation of stars, types of galaxies, structure and composition of the universe, scale of the universe, age and origin of the universe, current technology in astronomy, making careful observations, using evidence to support claims, using scientific knowledge, analyzing data, collecting observational data, sampling, organizing data, comparing and contrasting data, communicating plans, making recommendations.*

Answer the Big Question

Introducing PBIS

What Do Scientists Do?

1) Scientists...address big challenges and big questions.

You will find many different kinds of *Big Challenges* and *Questions* in *PBIS* Units. Some ask you to think about why something is a certain way. Some ask you to think about what causes something to change. Some challenge you to design a solution to a problem. Most of them are about things that can and do happen in the real world.

Understand the Big Challenge or Question

As you get started with each Unit, you will do activities that help you understand the *Big Question* or *Challenge* for that Unit. You will think about what you already know that might help you, and you will identify some of the new things you will need to learn.

Project Board

The *Project Board* helps you keep track of your learning. For each challenge or question, you will use a *Project Board* to keep track of what you know, what you need to learn, and what you are learning. As you learn and gather evidence, you will record that on the *Project Board*. After you have answered each small question or challenge, you will return to the *Project Board* to record how what you've learned helps you answer the *Big Question* or *Challenge*.

Learning Sets

Each Unit is composed of a group of *Learning Sets*, one for each of the smaller questions that need to be answered to address the *Big Question* or *Challenge*. In each *Learning Set*, you will investigate and read to find answers to the *Learning Set's* question. You will also have a chance to share the results of your investigations with your classmates and work together to make sense of what you are learning. As you come to understand answers to the questions on the *Project Board*, you will record those answers and the evidence you've collected. At the end of each *Learning Set*, you will apply your knowledge to the *Big Question* or *Challenge*.

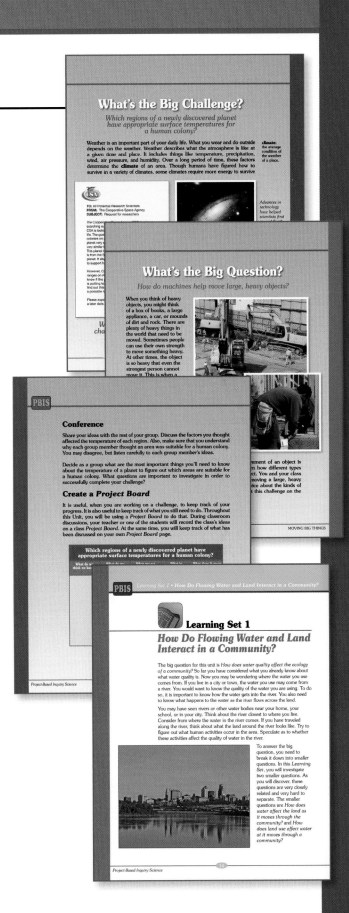

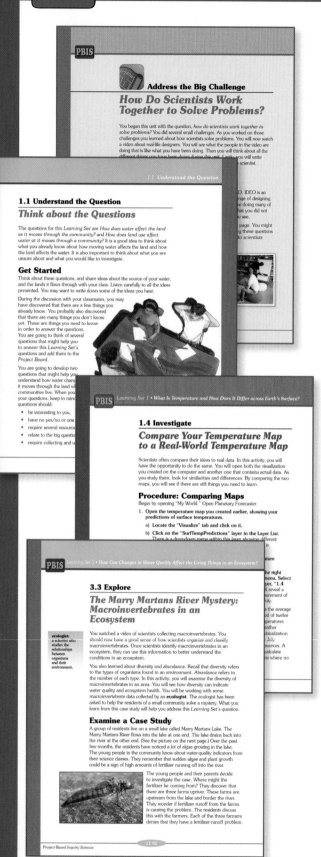

Answer the Big Question / Address the Big Challenge

At the end of each Unit, you will put everything you have learned together to tackle the *Big Question or Challenge*.

2) Scientists...address smaller questions and challenges.

What You Do in a Learning Set

Understanding the Question or Challenge

At the start of each *Learning Set*, you will usually do activities that will help you understand the *Learning Set's* question or challenge and recognize what you already know that can help you answer the question or achieve the challenge. Usually, you will visit the *Project Board* after these activities and record on it the even smaller questions that you need to investigate to answer a *Learning Set's* question.

Investigate/Explore

There are many different kinds of investigations you might do to find answers to questions. In the *Learning Sets*, you might

- design and run experiments;
- design and run simulations;
- design and build models;
- examine large sets of data.

Don't worry if you haven't done these things before. The text will provide you with lots of help in designing your investigations and in analyzing your data.

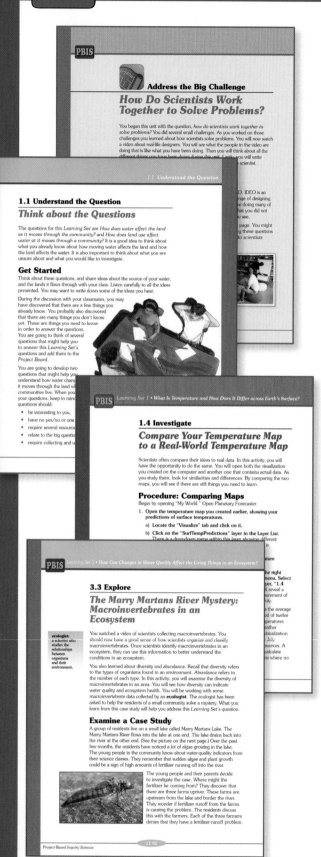

Address the Big Challenge

How Do Scientists Work Together to Solve Problems?

You began this unit with the question, *how do scientists work together to solve problems?* You did several small challenges. As you worked on those challenges you learned about how scientists solve problems. You will now watch a video about real-life designers. You will see what the people in the video are doing that is like what you have been doing. Then you will think about all the different things you have been doing during this unit.

1.1 Understand the Question

Think about the Questions

The questions for this *Learning Set* are *How does water affect the land as it moves through the community?* and *How does land use affect water at it moves through a community?* It is a good idea to think about what you already know about how moving water affects the land and how the land affects the water. It is also important to think about what you are unsure about and what you would like to investigate.

Get Started

Think about these questions, and share ideas about the source of your water, and the lands it flows through with your class. Listen carefully to all the ideas presented. You may want to write down some of the ideas you hear.

During the discussion with your classmates, you may have discovered that there are a few things you already know. You probably also discovered that there are many things you don't know yet. These are things you need to know in order to answer the questions. You are going to think of several questions that might help you to answer this *Learning Set's* questions and add them to the *Project Board*.

1.4 Investigate

Compare Your Temperature Map to a Real-World Temperature Map

Scientists often compare their ideas to real data. In this activity, you will have the opportunity to do the same. You will open both the visualization you created on the computer and another one that contains actual data. As you study them, look for similarities and differences. By comparing the two maps, you will see if there are still things you need to learn.

Procedure: Comparing Maps

Begin by opening "My World." Open Planetary Forecaster.

1. Open the temperature map you created earlier, showing your predictions of surface temperatures.

a) Locate the "Visualize" tab and click on it.

b) Click on the "SurfTempPredictions" layer in the Layer List.

3.3 Explore

The Marry Martans River Mystery: Macroinvertebrates in an Ecosystem

ecologist: a scientist who studies the relationships between organisms and their environment.

You watched a video of scientists collecting macroinvertebrates. You should now have a good sense of how scientists organize and classify macroinvertebrates. Once scientists identify macroinvertebrates in an ecosystem, they can use this information to better understand the conditions in an ecosystem.

You also learned about diversity and abundance. Recall that diversity refers to the types of organisms found in an environment. Abundance refers to the number of each type. In this activity, you will examine the diversity of macroinvertebrates in an area. You will see how diversity can indicate water quality and ecosystem health. You will be working with some macroinvertebrate data collected by an **ecologist**. The ecologist has been asked to help the residents of a small community solve a mystery. What you learn from this case study will help you address this *Learning Set's* question.

Examine a Case Study

A group of residents live on a small lake called Marry Martans Lake. The Marry Martans River flows into the lake at one end. The lake drains back into the river at the other end. (See the picture on the next page.) Over the past few months, the residents have noticed a lot of algae growing in the lake. The young people in the community know about water-quality indicators from their science classes. They remember that sudden algae and plant growth could be a sign of high amounts of fertilizer running off into the river.

The young people and their parents decide to investigate the case. Where might the fertilizer be coming from? They discover that there are three farms upriver. These farms are upstream from the lake and border the river. They wonder if fertilizer runoff from the farms is causing the problem. The residents discuss this with the farmers. Each of the three farmers denies that they have a fertilizer-runoff problem.

Read

Like scientists, you will also read about the science you are learning. You'll read a little bit before you investigate, but most of the reading you do will be to help you understand what you've experienced or seen in an investigation. Each time you read, the text will include *Stop and Think* questions after the reading. These questions will help you gauge how well you understand what you have read. Usually, the class will discuss the answers to *Stop and Think* questions before going on so that everybody has a chance to make sense of the reading.

Design and Build

When the *Big Challenge* for a Unit asks you to design something, the challenge in a *Learning Set* might also ask you to design something and make it work. Often, you will design a part of the thing you will design and build for the *Big Challenge*. When a *Learning Set* challenges you to design and build something, you will do several things:

- identify what questions you need to answer to be successful

- investigate to find answers to those questions

- use those answers to plan a good design solution

- build and test your design.

Because designs don't always work the way you want them to, you will usually do a design challenge more than once. Each time through, you will test your design. If your design doesn't work as well as you'd like, you will determine why it is not working and identify other things you need to investigate to make it work better. Then, you will learn those things and try again.

Explain and Recommend

A big part of what scientists do is explain, or try to make sense of why things happen the way they do. An explanation describes why something is the way it is or behaves the way it does. An explanation is a statement you make built from claims (what you think you know), evidence (from an investigation) that supports the claim, and science knowledge. As they learn, scientists get better at explaining. You'll see that you get better, too, as you work through the *Learning Sets*.

A recommendation is a special kind of claim—one where you advise somebody about what to do. You will make recommendations and support them with evidence, science knowledge, and explanations.

ASTRONOMY

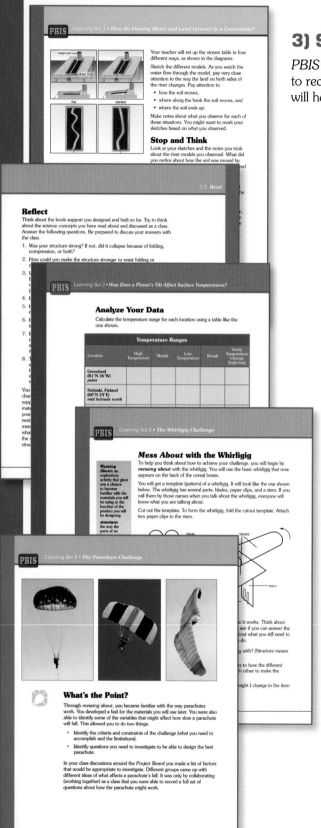

3) Scientists...reflect in many different ways.

PBIS provides guidance to help you think about what you are doing and to recognize what you are learning. Doing this often as you are working will help you be a successful student scientist.

Tools for Making Sense

Stop and Think

Stop and Think sections help you make sense of what you've been doing in the section you are working on. *Stop and Think* sections include a set of questions to help you understand what you've just read or done. Sometimes the questions will remind you of something you need to pay more attention to. Sometimes they will help you connect what you've just read to things you already know. When there is a *Stop and Think* in the text, you will work individually or with a partner to answer the questions, and then the whole class will discuss the answers.

Reflect

Reflect sections help you connect what you've just done with other things you've read or done earlier in the Unit (or in another Unit). When there is a *Reflect* in the text, you will work individually, with a partner or your small group to answer the questions. Then, the whole class will discuss the answers. You may be asked to answer *Reflect* questions for homework.

Analyze Your Data

Whenever you have to analyze data, the text will provide hints about how to do that and what to look for.

Mess About

"Messing about" is a term that comes from design. It means exploring the materials you will be using for designing or building something or examining something that works like what you will be designing. Messing about helps you discover new ideas—and it can be a lot of fun. The text will usually give you ideas about things to notice as you are messing about.

What's the Point?

At the end of each *Learning Set*, you will find a summary, called *What's the Point?*, of the important information from the *Learning Set*. These summaries can help you remember how what you did and learned is connected to the *Big Question or Challenge* you are working on.

4) Scientists...collaborate.

Scientists never do all their work alone. They work with other scientists (collaborate) and share their knowledge. *PBIS* helps you be a student scientist by giving you lots of opportunities for sharing your findings, ideas, and discoveries with others (the way scientists do). You will work together in small groups to investigate, design, explain, and do other things. Sometimes you will work in pairs to figure out things together. You will also have lots of opportunities to share your findings with the rest of your classmates and make sense together of what you are learning.

Investigation Expo

In an *Investigation Expo*, small groups report to the class about an investigation they've done. For each *Investigation Expo*, you will make a poster detailing what you were trying to learn from your investigation, what you did, your data, and your interpretation of your data. The text gives you hints about what to present and what to look for in other groups' presentations. *Investigation Expos* are always followed by discussions about the investigations and about how to do science well. You may also be asked to write a lab report following an investigation.

Plan Briefing/Solution Briefing/Idea Briefing

Briefings are presentations of work in progress. They give you a chance to get advice from your classmates that can help you move forward. During a *Plan Briefing*, you present your plan to the class. It might be a plan for an experiment or a plan for solving a problem or achieving a challenge. During a *Solution Briefing*, you present your solution in progress and ask the class to help you make your solution better. During an *Idea Briefing*, you present your ideas. You get the best advice from your classmates when you present evidence in support of your plan, solution, or idea. Often, you will prepare a poster to help you make your presentation. Briefings are almost always followed by discussions of your investigations and how you will move forward.

Solution Showcase

Solution Showcases usually appear near the end of a Unit. During a *Solution Showcase*, you show your classmates your finished product—either your answer to a question or your solution to a challenge. You also tell the class why you think it is a good answer or solution, what evidence and science you used to get to your solution, and what you tried along the way before getting to your answer or solution. Sometimes a *Solution Showcase* is followed by a competition. It is almost always followed by a discussion comparing and contrasting the different answers and solutions groups have come up with. You may be asked to write a report or paper following a *Solution Showcase*.

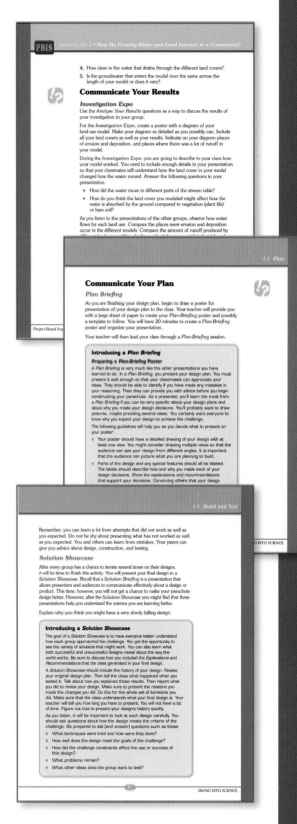

Update the Project Board

Remember that the *Project Board* is designed to help the class keep track of what they are learning and their progress towards a Unit's *Big Question* or *Challenge*. At the beginning of each Unit, the class creates a *Project Board*, and together you record what you think you know about answering the *Big Question* or addressing the *Big Challenge* and what you think you need to investigate further. Near the beginning of each *Learning Set*, the class revisits the *Project Board* and adds new questions and things they think they know. At the end of each *Learning Set*, the class again revisits the *Project Board*. This time you record what you have learned, the evidence you've collected, and recommendations you can make about answering the *Big Question* or achieving the *Big Challenge*.

Conference

A *Conference* is a short discussion between a small group of students before a more formal whole-class discussion. Students might discuss predictions and observations, they might try to explain together, they might consult on what they think they know, and so on. Usually, a *Conference* is followed by a discussion around the *Project Board*. In these small group discussions, everybody gets a chance to participate.

 What's the Point? Review what you have learned in each *Learning Set*.

 Stop and Think Answer questions that help you understand what you've done in a section.

Communicate Share your ideas and results with your classmates.

 Record Record your data as you gather it.

ASTRONOMY

As a Student Scientist, you will...

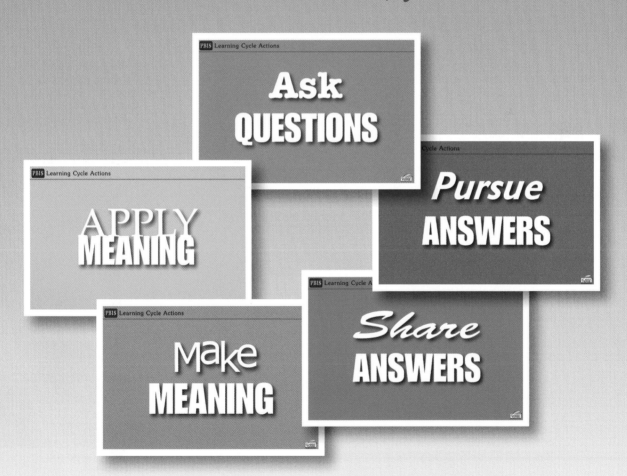

What's the Big Question?

How Can You Know if Objects in Space Will Collide?

You have spent every day of your life on the planet called Earth. Without leaving Earth, you wake up, go to school, sleep, work, and play. Every day the Sun appears to move across the sky and then moves below the horizon as night approaches. You know that the Sun is very important to life on Earth. But Earth and the Sun are just two of the many important objects in our **solar system**. The solar system is like Earth's neighborhood. This neighborhood includes the Sun, eight planets and their moons, and all the other bodies that **revolve** around the Sun.

What other solar-system objects do you know about? What do **astronomers**, the scientists who study space and objects in space, know about the movements of these objects, and how do they predict these movements? How can they use their predictions to learn more?

Scientists learn about the solar system by making observations and collecting data. Astronomers, and other scientists, are gaining exciting new knowledge every day through the use of powerful telescopes and space probes speeding through the solar system.

Whenever scientists collect data, they are trying to answer questions. One question for astronomers today is how the objects in our solar system formed. In space, beyond our solar system, scientists have learned about stars. They have also observed places where stars and other planetary systems form.

Many movies, television shows, and books have featured the idea of objects from space colliding with Earth. In some of these stories, people and countries unite to stop a collision with Earth, and the world is saved. In others, the results of these collisions are disastrous and life on Earth is forever changed. All of these movies, television programs, and books are *science fiction,* or made-up stories that describe possible events resulting from advances in science or technology. Other stories are set in imaginary environments, such as alien planets or other solar systems.

solar system: a Sun and the planets, comets, asteroids, and other bodies that revolve around it.

revolve: to move in a curved path determined by gravity of another object.

astronomer: a scientist who studies space and objects in space.

Are collisions with objects from space a real threat? If so, can anything be done to prevent these collisions from happening? What objects have the potential to collide? To answer these questions, you must be able to separate science fact from science fiction. Facts are evidence that can be used to support or oppose a hypothesis or explanation. Fiction is invented in someone's imagination. The purpose of fiction is to entertain people. Scientists work only with facts.

In this Unit, you will gather facts and perform investigations to help you answer this *Big Question: How Can You Know if Objects in Space Will Collide?*

Welcome to Astronomy.
Enjoy your journey as a student scientist.

Think About the *Big Question*

On Friday, October 9, 1992, at 7:50 PM, Michelle Knapp, a high school senior in Peekskill, New York, heard a loud crash outside her home. Rushing out of her house to investigate the noise, Michelle found that the trunk of her car had been demolished by a football-sized rock.

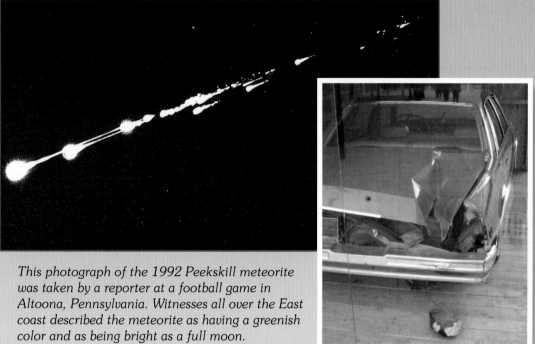

This photograph of the 1992 Peekskill meteorite was taken by a reporter at a football game in Altoona, Pennsylvania. Witnesses all over the East coast described the meteorite as having a greenish color and as being bright as a full moon.

Notice the football-sized rock under the damaged car. The rock weighed 12 kg, had a melted appearance, and was warm to the touch when found.

The front edge of the 12-kilogram rock had a melted appearance. When Michelle touched the rock, it was still warm. Red paint from her car was embedded in the rock. There was also a 15 cm (6 in) deep crater in the driveway under the rock.

The evidence in the previous paragraph suggested that the rock was a **meteorite**. A meteorite is a rock that travels from space through Earth's atmosphere and strikes Earth's surface. When a meteorite plows through Earth's atmosphere, the heat generated produces a thin, glassy coating on the outside of the meteorite called the *fusion crust*. The warmth of the rock, when Michelle touched it, was another good clue that the rock had heated up traveling through Earth's atmosphere. The crater under the car was further evidence that the rock had fallen from the sky.

meteorite: an object that enters Earth's atmosphere at high speed and reaches the ground without burning up.

That evening, several video cameras at high school football games shifted upward and recorded glimpses of an object streaking across the night sky. Later that evening, local television stations broadcast the videos of this unusual object. The videos showed a fireball breaking up into pieces. Scientists estimate that the original object may have been up to one meter in diameter with a mass as great as 25,000 kg (55,000 lb). Michelle's car was hit by the meteorite only moments after videos captured images of the object streaking through the night sky. The object that struck the car is now known as the Peekskill meteorite.

This story is a rare, firsthand account of a collision with an object from space. To answer the *Big Question* in this Unit, you will start by thinking about some more common types of collisions. To help you get started, you will watch some different collisions in action. As you make observations, think about how these crashes happen, what happens to the bodies that are colliding, and what you might be able to do to stop the collisions from happening.

Get Started

You will watch a short video. As you watch the video, pay close attention to the collisions and the effect the collisions have on the objects involved. Watch carefully as objects of different speeds collide with each other. What is the result of these collisions?

Conference

Share your ideas about the collisions in this video with your group. Describe what you saw when the objects collided with each other. Focus on the damage the collisions caused. What do you think would happen if the two objects were of very different sizes? What do you think was the effect of speed on the damage done by each collision? Could some of the collisions have been prevented? If so, how? Make a short list of questions and ideas about collisions that this video made you think about.

Also, think about what you know about objects in space. Would any of the objects you know about be likely to collide? Why or why not? Think about what you know about how these objects move to determine if they could collide, and what you still need to learn.

Communicate

Share Your Ideas

Share your questions and ideas about collisions with the class. Make a list of questions so that you will be able to remember them. Share your ideas and questions about objects from space that might collide. List those as well so you will remember them clearly.

Tennis Ball Demolition Derby

Cars in a demolition derby crash into each other, resulting in loud noises, dented metal, and jolts to the drivers. These collisions differ depending on how fast the cars are moving and how they strike one another. To help you answer some of your questions about collisions, you will explore the motion of tennis balls as they collide.

You will consider two types of motion: *random motion* and *ordered motion*. Each person in your class will roll a ball and you will make observations about the differences in the collisions when the motion is random and when it is somewhat organized. Each time you roll the balls, they will have a chance to collide. As you watch each type of motion, pay attention to how predictable the collisions are.

Materials

- tennis balls, 1 per student

Predict

Before doing the activity, read the entire procedure and predict which trial will have more collisions. Make predictions, too, about where collisions will occur and which trial might have more violent collisions.

Procedure

1. Each person in your class will get one ball. With your classmates, sit in a large circle. Without speaking or letting anyone know where you are going to roll the ball, choose a person in the circle, and prepare to roll the ball to them. When you hear the count, "Three, two, one, go!" all the balls should be rolled at the same time. Observe the movement of your ball and count the number of collisions your ball makes as it rolls along the floor. Write this number on a piece of paper and label it "Trial 1."

2. Then, repeat the same exercise, but this time you will roll a ball to one specific classmate, and *another* classmate will roll a ball to you. To start, each person will be given a number. You will count that number of places away from you, moving clockwise (left) around the circle. For example, if you were given the number *ten,* you would count ten places away from you, starting with the person on your left. You would roll the ball to the tenth person. Be sure the correct person knows he or she is receiving the ball from you. A different person will be rolling the ball to you. Check with that person, too. On the count of *three,* all the balls should be rolled at the same time. Observe the movement of your ball and count the collisions your ball makes as it rolls across the floor. Write this number on a piece of paper and label it "Trial 2."

Communicate

Share Your Results

Record on the board each student's count of the number of collisions in Trial 1 and Trial 2. As a class, compare the total number of collisions that occurred in Trial 1 with the total number in Trial 2. Also, look at the data to see if there are any trends. Discuss any differences in the timing or nature of the collisions during the two rolls.

Reflect

Use the results of your investigation to answer these questions with your group. Be prepared to share your answers with the class.

1. Did the results match your predictions? Why or why not?

2. Compare the collisions of the two trials in more detail. How were the collisions in the two trials similar to each other? How were they different? Were the collisions more violent in one trial? Where did most collisions occur in each trial? In each trial, how did early collisions affect later collisions?

3. What do you think would happen to the number of collisions if everyone had rolled two tennis balls each time?

4. What do you think would happen to the number of the collisions if the number of balls stayed the same but people sat in a circle that was three times bigger?

5. Is there any way to predict when specific collisions will occur in either trial? Why or why not?

6 How do you think the motion of the balls might compare to the way in which objects move and collide in the solar system?

7. Now that you know more about collisions, answer this question again: Are any of the objects you know about in space likely to collide? Why or why not?

Introducing the *Big Question*

The Big Question for this Unit is: How Can You Know if Objects in Space Will Collide? To answer this question you are going to have to understand how objects in the solar system move, how likely they are to collide with one another, and what happens when objects collide. You will also investigate objects outside the solar system to see if they could possibly collide with objects in our solar system. You will start by examining the evidence as Michelle and others did after the meteorite struck her car. Besides looking at past collisions, you will explore the motion of objects in space to investigate the likelihood of collisions in the future.

When you have completed this Unit, you will use what you have learned about how scientists know if two space objects will collide to develop an idea for a movie. To interest a movie producer in making a realistic movie about the possible collision of two space objects, you will need to put together all the information you gather in the *Learning Sets* as well as the results of all your investigations.

In your "pitch" to the movie producer, you will suggest space objects that might realistically collide, support your suggestion with an explanation of what makes the collision realistic, and a description of what such a collision might look like. You will also need to describe how such a collision would affect Earth, or other space object. The best idea will be one that is realistic, dramatic, and could affect Earth, or our Sun and Moon.

Reflect

Discuss the answers to these questions with your group. Sharing your answers with the class will prepare you to begin a *Project Board* for this Unit.

1. What do you already know that might be useful in answering the *Big Question?*

2. Examine the list of questions your class made earlier. Which of those questions need to be answered to answer the *Big Question?*

3. What other questions do you need to know answers to so that you can answer the *Big Question* and write your report?

Create a *Project Board*

When working on any challenge, it is useful to keep track of your progress. It is also helpful to keep track of what you still need to do. Throughout this Unit, you will use a *Project Board* for this purpose. During classroom discussions, one person in the class will record ideas and questions on a class *Project Board*. At the same time, you will keep track of what has been discussed on your own *Project Board* page.

Recall that a *Project Board* has space for answering five guiding questions:

- What do we think we know?
- What do we need to investigate?
- What are we learning?
- What is our evidence?
- What does it mean for the challenge or question?

How can you know if objects in space will collide?				
What do we think we know?	What do we need to investigate?	What are we learning?	What is our evidence?	What does it mean for the challenge or question?

To get started on this *Project Board,* you need to identify and record the important science question you will address for this Unit: *How can you know if objects in space will collide?* Record this question at the top of the *Project Board.*

In the first column of the *Project Board,* record what you think you know about any objects in the solar system that may collide. You discussed this among your groups during your earlier conference. Use the ideas your group came up with to make suggestions for the *Project Board.* Perhaps you have studied or read about some of these objects before. Even if it is a small fact or idea, talk about it. Discuss any factors that you think might be helpful in working toward the completion of your project.

In the second column, record what you need to investigate. Again, you discussed these things in your conference and you made a class list. During your conference, you may have found that you and others in your group did not agree on some ideas. This second column is designed to help you keep track of things that are debatable, unknown, or need to be investigated to answer the *Big Question*.

Later in this Unit, you will return to the *Project Board*. For now, work with your classmates as you begin to record ideas and suggestions in the first two columns.

What's the Point?

Before starting on the exploration of any new idea, it is helpful to try to understand what the goals are for your investigations. You have discussed some general ideas about collisions. You have applied that knowledge to what you already know about the solar system. You have used your current knowledge to come up with more questions that need to be answered. You know that the goal of your investigations is to learn how scientists can know if objects in the solar system will collide. If you keep this goal in mind as you make your explorations, you will stay on track all the way to answering a big and important question for us all.

Learning Set 1

Have Objects in the Solar System Collided?

The *Big Question* for this Unit is *How Can You Know if Objects in Space Will Collide?* To help you answer this question, you will break it down into smaller questions and answer those. In this *Learning Set,* you are going to answer the question, *Have objects in the solar system collided?* Scientists can only know about collisions if evidence of a collision is available. To answer the question for this *Learning Set,* you will use the same evidence scientists have used to decide if solar system objects have collided. That evidence will help you support a claim about whether collisions have occurred.

Do you see the "Man in the Moon" or the "Rabbit on the Moon"? Without a telescope or binoculars, you can only imagine what the bright spots and dark areas are.

The Moon is Earth's closest neighbor in the solar system. From early history, people have looked at the Moon and tried to explain the surface features they could see. Someone has probably pointed out the "Man in the Moon" to you. Some cultures have described the Moon's features as looking like a rabbit with a bright tail. If you look for the "Rabbit on the Moon," you will likely see bright spots and large dark areas that form an image of the creature, but without binoculars or a telescope, you cannot tell what these spots and areas really are. The invention of the telescope in 1608 allowed the astronomer Galileo Galilei to be among the first to see details of the Moon's surface. It was Galileo's detailed description of a large "hole" that made people curious about the Moon's **craters**. Craters are rounded depressions on the surface of any solid body in the solar system.

crater: a rounded depression in the surface of a planet, moon, or solid body.

Scientists began to study the Moon's craters soon after Galileo's discovery. They wondered how the craters were formed. In 1892, the American scientist Grove Karl Gilbert proposed that most craters were caused by impacts made by other, smaller bodies. (Scientists often use the word "body" to refer to objects in space.) Gilbert ran many experiments to determine how craters were formed. You will soon be performing one of the same experiments Gilbert used to gather evidence for his claim.

After the invention of the telescope in 1608, scientists could see what the large "holes" were on the Moon. These early astronomers did not know what caused these "holes," or craters.

1.1 Understand the Question

Think About What Happens When Objects Collide

The question for this *Learning Set* is *Have objects in the solar system collided?* Before you can answer this question, you must first consider what happens when objects collide.

Get Started

You will simulate an impact between an object and the Moon's surface. You will use a plastic tub of flour and colored powder to represent the Moon. Use the ruler and meter stick to make measurements as you record your observations.

You will model what happens when different objects strike the Moon by observing what happens when different objects strike the flour in the tub. You may use any object that can safely be dropped into the plastic tub. Be imaginative about the types of objects you use. You may throw objects so that they strike the flour at an angle, but do not do so in a dangerous way.

Begin by making a chart like the one below. It should have three columns, one to describe the object being dropped or thrown into the tub, one to describe how it was dropped or thrown, and one to record what the flour looks like after the impact.

Materials
- **plastic tub filled with flour**
- cocoa powder
- ruler
- meter stick
- objects to drop into the flour
- impact glasses

Object, including its size and shape	How the object was dropped or thrown	What the flour looks like after the impact

Be careful when you throw objects at an angle. Make sure you throw them only into the container holding the flour. Do not throw the objects harder than necessary for them to land in the tub.

Begin by sprinkling colored powder over the white flour. This will make it easy for you to track what happens to the flour when it is hit by an object. Take turns dropping objects on the flour. After each object is dropped or thrown at the flour, record what the object was, how it was dropped onto the flour, and the pattern made by the colored powder. Smooth out the flour and sprinkle more colored powder into the tub after each impact so that the tub has an even surface before each impact.

Record the shape of the surface in the tub after each collision and the pattern made by the colored powder. Each member of your group should take two turns dropping or throwing an object onto the flour.

Communicate

Share Your Observations

Discuss your observations as a class. Talk about what you found interesting and what questions the activity helped you think about. Consider the following questions in your discussion:

- How did the effects of the impact change as the conditions of the collision changed?

- Was the object affected by the impact?

- After the impact, what evidence was left that a collision occurred?

- What factors do you think affect the size and shape of the crater made by a collision?

- How do you think these collisions are similar to collisions on the Moon?

- What questions do you need to answer to know for sure which factors affect the size and shape of a crater caused by a collision?

- What questions do you need to answer before you can answer the bigger question, *Have objects in the solar system collided?*

Update the *Project Board*

In the *What do we think we know?* column, record what you think
you know about the effects of collisions. In the *What do we need to
investigate?* column, record questions that will resolve any disagreements
your class had about collisions. Also record any questions you need to
investigate to know for sure which factors affect the size and shape of a
crater caused by a collision. Then record questions you need to answer to
help you understand whether objects in the solar system have collided.

How can you know if objects in space will collide?				
What do we think we know?	What do we need to investigate?	What are we learning?	What is our evidence?	What does it mean for the challenge or question?

ASTRONOMY

1.2 Investigate

Model a Collision With the Moon

impact crater: a crater formed when an object strikes a planet, moon, or solid body.

Scientists think that craters on the Moon were made by collisions with space objects. These kinds of craters are called **impact craters**. Impact craters are the direct result of a collision between an object and the surface of a planet, moon, or other solar-system body. But craters might happen for other reasons, too. Scientists can be sure a crater was caused by a collision with an object from space only if the size and shape of the crater is consistent with the kind of crater a collision would make.

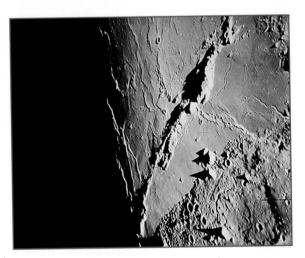

Looking at a photograph of the Moon, you can see that the craters are many different sizes. The craters vary in diameter (width across) and depth. By looking at shadows, you can tell how high the walls of a crater are, and therefore, how deep the crater is. Galileo observed and commented on shadows and the heights of mountains on the Moon when he recorded his telescope observations of the Moon. In this section, you will investigate and identify the factors that affect the size and shape of an impact crater. In experiments similar to those run by Grove Karl Gilbert, you will make craters using different types of objects. This will allow you to identify any patterns in the resulting craters. Later, you will use what you learned to decide which of the craters on the Moon and on Earth are impact craters.

Parts of an Impact Crater

Aristarchus Crater

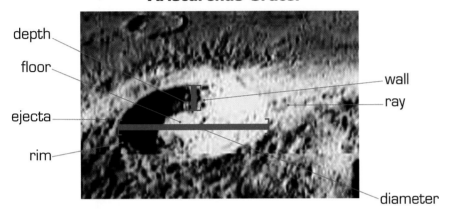

depth
floor
ejecta
rim
wall
ray
diameter

The Aristarchus Crater is an example of a large impact crater. Notice the different parts: the floor, rim, wall, ejecta, and ray. A crater is measured by its depth and diameter.

As you explore how craters are made, you may need to talk to others about what you are learning. Sharing ideas is easier when you have a common set of words to describe your craters.

floor: the bottom of the crater. It can be flat or bowl-shaped, and is usually below the surrounding ground level.

rim: the raised, circular formation surrounding the floor of the crater.

wall: the sides of the crater that rise to the rim.

depth: in a crater, the perpendicular (at right angles) measurement downward from the original ground level to the crater floor.

diameter: the length of a straight line from one side of a circular crater to the other, through the center point of the crater.

ejecta: the material thrown out of the crater during impact.

ray: a bright streak starting from the crater and extending for great distances.

variable: a quantity whose value may change (vary) over the course of an experiment.

hypothesis: a prediction of what will happen to a dependent (responding) variable when a change is made to the independent (manipulated) variable while other variables are held constant. A hypothesis is not a guess; it is always based on what you know.

independent (or manipulated) variable: in an experiment, a variable whose value is manipulated, or changed, by the experimenter, to observe its effects on another variable (the dependent or responding variable).

control variables: in an experiment, the variables that are kept constant (not changed).

Be a Scientist

Designing an Experiment

When investigating an event in nature, scientists want to learn about the factors that influence it. In science, these factors are called **variables**. For example, two factors that might affect the formation of a crater are the size and speed of the object impacting the surface. The point of running experiments is to understand how some variable affects the event you are investigating.

An experiment is designed to test a **hypothesis**. A hypothesis is a prediction based on observations. It is what you think is the most likely answer to a question. In many cases, the hypothesis will be a statement about how one variable is related to other variables in the experiment.

As you design and run your experiment, there are several kinds of variables with which you will work.

- In an experiment, the experimenter controls the value of one variable. This is the one that is changed or varied in your experiment. This is called the **independent variable** (or **manipulated variable**).

- Most other factors must be kept the same (constant) during every trial. These are called **controlled variables**. By holding these variables constant, the experimenter can be sure that the results are affected only by the changes in the independent variable.

- Factors that might change when the manipulated variable is changed are called **dependent variables** (or **responding variables**). Their values are dependent on the value of the independent, or manipulated, variable. These are the variables you measure after each trial.

When scientists design an experiment, they think about the factors that might affect the results of the experiment. Then they identify the variable about which they want to find out more. They choose this variable as the independent (manipulated) variable. This is the one they vary to identify its effects. The other variables that could affect the outcome must be kept the same, or controlled, each time the procedure is carried out. If the experiment is designed well, then changes in the dependent variables can be assumed to result from changes made to the independent variable.

You have investigated how some different objects form craters and observed the craters formed by each object. The class made a list of the factors that you think might affect the size and shape of a crater, but you do not know for sure what the effect of each factor will be.

You will begin by developing a hypothesis about how one factor, such as the size or mass of an object, or the angle at which it hits, affects the size and shape of a crater. Then you will select objects for your experiment that will allow you to gather information to test your hypothesis. For this experiment, you will use the same plastic tub you used earlier. You will again sprinkle a thin layer of colored powder over the surface of the flour and throw or drop objects into the flour. The colored flour will help you see the ejecta and rays of the craters. After each trial, you will smooth out the flour and sprinkle more colored powder on the surface.

dependent (or responding) variable: in an experiment, a variable whose value changes when the value of an independent variable is changed; also called the responding variable.

Design an Experiment

Each group in the class will be assigned a different factor to investigate and run an experiment to learn how that factor affects the shape and size of a crater. In your group, discuss and then design a good experiment to investigate the effects of your variable on a crater's shape and size. Remember to discuss and record the following aspects of your experiment's design.

Materials

- **plastic tub filled with flour, $\frac{3}{4}$" deep**
- **cocoa powder**
- **ruler**
- **meterstick**
- **objects to drop into the flour**
- **impact glasses**
- **presentation materials**

Question

What question are you investigating or answering with this experiment? For example, you might be answering the question, *How does the mass of the object striking a surface affect the length, width, and depth of the crater that forms?*

Prediction

What do you think is the answer to the question? Start by writing a hypothesis. Your hypothesis is your prediction about how your independent (manipulated) variable and a dependent (responding) variable are related. Hypotheses are written as statements that can be tested, often using a format like this: "If I [*increase/decrease*] the [*independent variable*], then the [*dependent variable*] will [*increase/decrease/stay the same*]." You write a different hypothesis statement for each dependent variable that you think will be affected by a change in your independent variable.

If the question is about three dependent variables (for example, length, width, and depth), you would develop three hypothesis statements. You would state each hypothesis as, "If I drop a ball with less mass in the flour, the result will be a crater with [*greater/less/the same*] [*length/width/depth*]."

Variable Identification

- Which variable will you manipulate (change) in your experiment?

- What conditions and procedures will you keep the same (hold constant or control) in your experiment?

- What characteristics of each crater will you observe or measure?

- How many trials will you do for each value of your manipulated variable?

Procedure and Data

Write detailed instructions for how to conduct the experiment. Include the following:

- what object or objects you will drop or throw into the tub

- how you will drop or throw the object

- how you will measure the resulting crater

- how many trials you will perform

Make sure you can explain to the class why you think they will be able to trust your data.

Use an *Impact Crater Experiment Planning Guide* page and *Impact Crater Experiment Results Guide* to plan and organize your experiment. Use the hints on the planning page as a guide. Be sure to write enough in each section so that you will be able to present your experiment design to the class. The class will want to know that you have thought through all the parts of your plan.

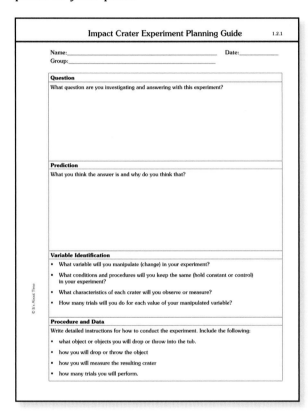

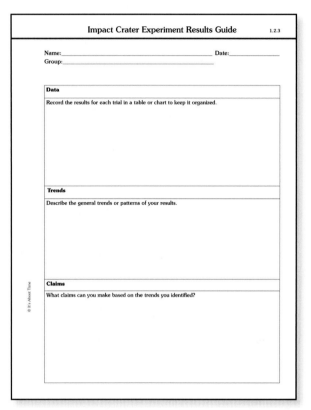

Communicate

Plan Briefing

As a group, present the plan for your experiment to the class. Discuss with the class ways to ensure that your experiment will successfully test your hypothesis and answer your question. Make sure your presentation answers the following questions:

- What question are you answering?

- What independent variable are you manipulating in your experiment?

What are you investigating about that variable? How are you going to vary it to determine its effects? What objects will you use, and how will you drop or throw those objects into the sand?

- List all of the variables you will hold constant in your experiment.

- How many trials will you perform?

- What measurements will you be making in your experiment? Why are these the right ones? What steps will you take to ensure that all measurements are made in exactly the same way?

As you listen, decide whether each group's experiment can answer the question they want to answer. Do you think they are doing a good enough job controlling variables? Are they measuring the right things and using a good measurement method? If you think you can help them make their experiment better, raise your hand and offer your advice. Remember to be respectful.

Run Your Experiment

Revise your procedure based on advice from the class, and then show your procedure to the teacher. After your teacher approves your procedure, use that procedure to run your experiment and test your hypothesis. Record your data. Data include numerical results as well as sketches and written notes on observations you made during the different trials.

Analyze Your Data

Data analysis is an opportunity to put your data in a form that will help you and others understand it. It is not just a restating of the data. For this experiment, you might make a graph of the data. For example, for the question, *How does the mass of the object affect the depth of the crater?* you may draw a graph with mass on the horizontal axis (*y*-axis) and depth on the vertical axis (*x*-axis). Drawing a graph may help you to see any patterns in how the two variables are related.

In your group, think about these questions to help you analyze your data:

1. How will you describe the relationships between the independent variable and the dependent variables?

2. How will you work with data from multiple trials that were run for each value of the independent variable? Will you include each trial on your graph or will you average the data for the trials?

3. How can you use sketches of the craters to help you analyze the data?

For each hypothesis you wrote, develop a conclusion about the relationship between the independent variable and the dependent variable. Make sure you have evidence from your data to support each conclusion you make.

Then draw the right graphs or charts to help others to interpret your data the same way you did and come to the same conclusions. Your graphs or charts must include all of your data.

Studying Craters

Earlier you learned that an impact crater is formed by an object striking a larger body. However, there is another kind of crater that is also present on some bodies in the solar system. A volcanic crater is a bowl-shaped depression that forms around the opening of a volcano. Volcanoes are openings in the surface of a body through which hotter material can flow or burst through. Often, a series of eruptions of this material creates a cone-shaped hill with a crater at the top.

Grove Karl Gilbert was an American scientist who studied craters on the Moon and Earth at the end of the nineteenth century. At the time, all of the known craters on Earth were thought to have been formed by volcanoes.

An impact crater (above right) is formed when an object strikes a larger body. A volcanic crater (right) is a bowl-shaped depression that forms around the opening of a volcano.

Grove Karl Gilbert conducted a series of experiments to study the structure of impact craters. He dropped clay balls into clay and sand. He also shot bullets into targets made of clay and sand. Using conclusions he formed after these experiments, he hypothesized that the large dark areas on the Moon were more likely to be impact craters than volcanic craters.

Gilbert was the first to realize that Mare Imbrium on the Moon (left) resembled an impact crater more than a volcano.

Communicate Your Results

Investigation Expo

You will share the results and analysis of your investigation with other groups in an *Investigation Expo*. For your presentation, make a poster that includes the following information:

- the question you were answering in your investigation

- your hypothesis and why you made this hypothesis

- your independent variable and the values you gave it

- your dependent variables and how you measured each

- your procedure, including the variables you controlled

- your data, including measurements, notes, and sketches of the craters

- your data analysis

- your conclusion or conclusions

Begin your presentation by stating your question, your hypothesis, your independent and dependent variables, and the reasons you chose those variables. Share with the class how you changed the independent variable and the results of each change. Use the sketches you made to show the effects of the change on the size, shape, or other features of the crater. As you describe the changes, use the language you have learned that describes each feature of a crater. Complete your presentation by sharing your conclusions.

As you listen, make sure you agree with the conclusions of each group. If you do not think that a group's data support their conclusion, raise your hand and explain why. If you have identified a different conclusion, tell the class what your conclusion is. After scientists give presentations, they have these kinds of discussions. Remember that the purpose of the discussion is to learn as much as you can about the effects of different factors on the size and shape of impact craters.

As each group makes its presentation, make a class list of the variables that were tested and the effects of each. When all the presentations are complete, discuss the variables each group tested to determine, as a class, which have the greatest effect on the size, shape, and other features of impact craters.

Reflect

Answer each question based on the data your class collected.

1. What conclusions can you draw about how the size of an object affects the size and shape of the crater it forms?

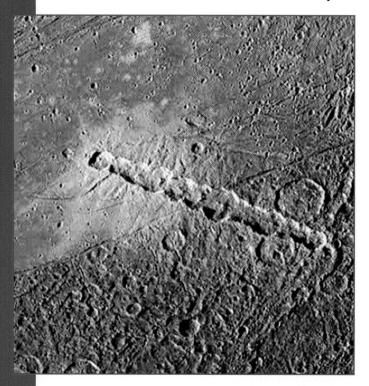

2. What conclusions can you draw about how the mass of an object affects the size and shape of the crater it forms?

3. Some groups varied the height from which they dropped their object. How does changing this variable affect the craters that were formed?

4. What conclusions can you make about how the speed of an object affects the size and shape of the crater it forms?

5. What conclusions can you make about how the angle at which an object impacts a surface affects the size and shape of the crater that is formed?

6. Can you think of other variables you may want to test to see if they affect the characteristics of an impact crater?

A chain of craters found on Ganymede, a moon of the planet Jupiter.

7. The photograph above shows a chain of thirteen closely spaced craters on Ganymede, a moon of the planet Jupiter. What do you think could have caused this series of craters? How many different ideas can you develop to account for these craters?

What's the Point?

When an object collides with another object, a crater may form. The angle and speed at which an object hits and the mass and size of the object all affect the size and features of the crater.

There are many craters on the Moon's surface, and they vary greatly in size and depth. Using what you now know about impact craters, you will be able to decide if the craters on the Moon were caused by impacts or caused some other way.

1.3 Explore

What Are the Characteristics of Craters on the Moon?

You investigated how impact craters are formed and what affects their size and shape. You observed that the mass of an object affects the depth and diameter of a crater more than the shape. You may also have observed that most impact craters are round, even if they are created by irregularly shaped objects. The angle at which an object hits a surface can affect the appearance of the crater and ejecta. Objects hitting at a low angle can create a piling up of ejecta at one end of the crater. This can make the crater somewhat oval in shape.

An impact crater is like a collision record. In many cases, the object that caused the collision is destroyed or cannot be directly observed. However, the crater itself is a powerful tool for figuring out the motion and characteristics of the object that caused the collision. Using reasoning to reenact the conditions that led to a collision is an important tool in understanding what object could cause such a collision, predicting when collisions will occur, and predicting what will happen after a collision occurs.

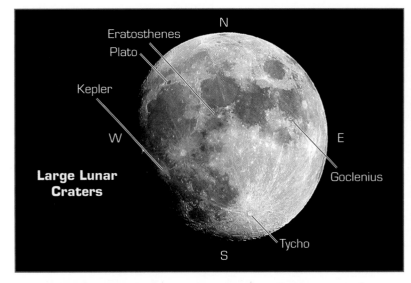

Lunar craters have been mapped since the invention of the telescope in 1608. As technology and space exploration have improved, these maps have become more accurate.

The Moon's surface is covered with craters. Scientists study these craters to learn about the history of the Moon and what happens when impacts occur. From Earth, the craters may look small, but many are hundreds of kilometers across. To help you understand the size of these craters, it is helpful to compare them to something with which you are more familiar on Earth.

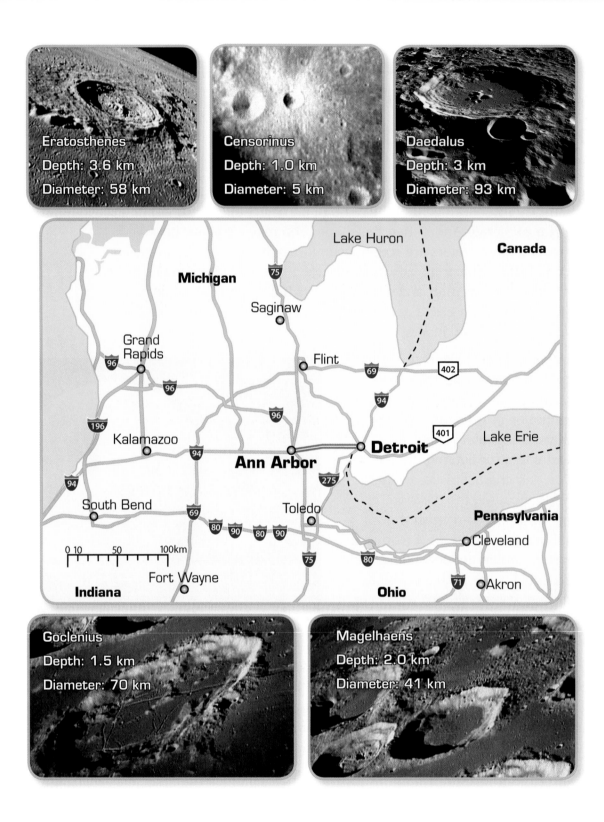

Eratosthenes
Depth: 3.6 km
Diameter: 58 km

Censorinus
Depth: 1.0 km
Diameter: 5 km

Daedalus
Depth: 3 km
Diameter: 93 km

Goclenius
Depth: 1.5 km
Diameter: 70 km

Magelhaens
Depth: 2.0 km
Diameter: 41 km

Procedure

With your partner, observe the pictures of different lunar craters. The diameter of each one is given in kilometers. For the diameter of each crater, use a map to find a landmark on Earth that is the same distance from where you are right now. For example, the diameter of *Goclenius* is about 70 km. Look at the map on the previous page. If you were sitting in a school in Detroit, Michigan, the edge of this crater would end in Ann Arbor, Michigan, about 70 km away.

Reflect

1. After carefully observing each picture, compare these craters with those made in the experiments. Use characteristics of each crater, such as shape, ejecta, and size, to decide whether each is an impact crater or not. Which ones are impact craters? How do you know?

2. Compare the craters in the pictures. How are they the same? How are they different?

3. Most of the lunar craters you have observed are rather large. Think back to the experiment you did and apply what you learned to the formation of craters on the Moon. What can you infer about the size of the objects that collided with the Moon to make these craters?

4. Construct a description of the event that caused each impact crater you analyzed. Include your best guess for the size, speed, and angle of the object that collided with the Moon to form the crater.

Craters on the Moon

Based on the results of your experiment in the preceding section, you know that objects with more mass create craters with greater depth and diameter. By applying what you learned from the experiment, you can say that a crater such as *Daedalus* (depth: 3 km, diameter: 93 km) resulted from a collision with an object with much more mass than the object that created *Censorinus* (depth: 1 km, diameter: 5 km). However, it is also important to look at other variables, possibly tested by your classmates, that could also have an effect on the crater's size and shape.

The angle at which an object strikes the surface affects the depth of the crater. An object that collides with the Moon at a small angle will not make a crater as deep as an object that crashes head on into the Moon. The angle will also affect the rays of the crater. More material will be thrown away from the impact in the same direction in which the object was moving, and less material will be thrown backward. Therefore, the relative length of the rays and the direction of the longest ray from a crater can help determine the direction and angle of the object's motion before the collision.

These lunar craters resulted from the impact of objects of various masses and speeds, hitting the surface at many different angles.

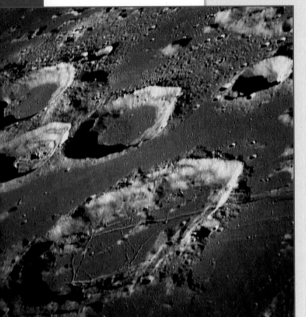

In your experiment, you may have found that objects crashing at a small angle form oval craters. All of the craters on the Moon are nearly circular. Objects that collide at high speed form circular craters, even if they strike at small angles. This happens because the surface of the larger object and the impacting object behave like liquids during high-speed collisions.

The speed of an object also affects other characteristics of a crater. Objects that are moving faster will form impact craters that are larger and deeper. The size of an object is not as important as its mass and speed in determining the size of the crater. In your experiment, if you gently dropped objects from a height of a few feet, the size of the crater closely matched the size of the object. When objects strike from a greater distance with greater speed, however, the size of the object is less important to the crater's size than is its distance and speed.

What's the Point?

Measurements of the diameter and depth of the craters can help you comprehend how big the craters are. Making a comparison to a common distance, such as the distance between two cities, can help you imagine the depth and width of a crater.

The most important factors for determining what the diameter of an impact crater on a solar-system body will be the mass and speed of the impacting object. These two factors, as well as the angle at which an object hits, determine the depth of the crater.

1.4 Explore

Does Earth Have Craters Formed by Collisions With Space Objects?

When you look at pictures of the Moon, the entire surface seems covered with craters. If there have been collisions on Earth as well, why isn't Earth covered with craters? You may never have seen an impact crater on Earth, even if you have traveled all around the world. And, you do not know for sure if Earth has such craters. If Earth has even a few craters like those on the Moon, they should be easy to find using **satellite images**. You will use an Earth-imaging program to explore Earth's surface, looking for evidence of craters.

satellite image: an image taken by an artificial object placed in orbit around Earth.

A crater is evidence of a past collision only when it is an impact crater, not a volcanic crater. You must determine what type of crater you are looking at before you can determine if it is evidence of a collision. As it turns out, all of the craters on the Moon are the result of impacts. But the same cannot be said about the craters on Earth.

You can use Earth-imaging software to inspect satellite images of Earth. The program will allow you to scroll east, west, north, and south, and also to zoom in and zoom out. The program will enable you to record the coordinates (latitude and longitude) of specific points on each image.

Looking for Craters Near You

Procedure

1. Find a familiar landmark, such as your home or school. Use the navigation tools to explore the nearby area, searching for evidence of craters.

2. Record the location of any craters you find using longitude and latitude. Make a sketch of the crater and label it with the parts you find.

Finding a Crater

Procedure

3. Enter *Meteor Crater in Arizona* into the search box of the program you are using. Wait until this area appears clearly on the map. This crater is also known as Barringer Meteorite Crater.

4. Explore the crater using the navigation tools. Scroll around the rim of the crater and record the different elevations, usually shown near the bottom of the screen. Scroll over the floor of the crater and record those elevations. Locate the rim, bowl, floor, and ejecta. Sketch the crater and label each crater part that you can observe.

> **The Barringer Meteorite Crater (Meteor Crater)**
> Meteor Crater is located in the middle of an Arizona desert. The crater is 1.3 km wide (0.8 mi) and 174 m deep (570 ft). This means that the crater is about as deep as a six-story building and as wide across as 14 football fields. Scientists agree that it was created by an impact from a meteorite that survived its trip through Earth's atmosphere.
>
>
>
> The meteorite that formed this crater struck Earth about 50,000 years ago, during the last Ice Age. The meteorite was only about 50 m (164 ft) across, about half a city block. Evidence from the crater indicates that the meteorite was made of the metals nickel and iron, and it had a mass greater than 100,000 tons. A 100,000-ton meteorite has the same mass as 15,000 large elephants or 400 Statues of Liberty.
>
> An impact that massive would have created a large crater and explosion. Scientists have calculated that the impact of the meteorite as it collided with Earth produced an explosion equal to over 20 million tons of

explosives. The blast was so strong that every living thing in a wide area around the impact crater was surely affected. Most plants and animals in a 3 km (almost 2 mi) radius were likely killed. The winds created by the impact were probably strong enough to flatten trees as far away as 20 km (12 mi). Most of the meteorite was destroyed in the explosion.

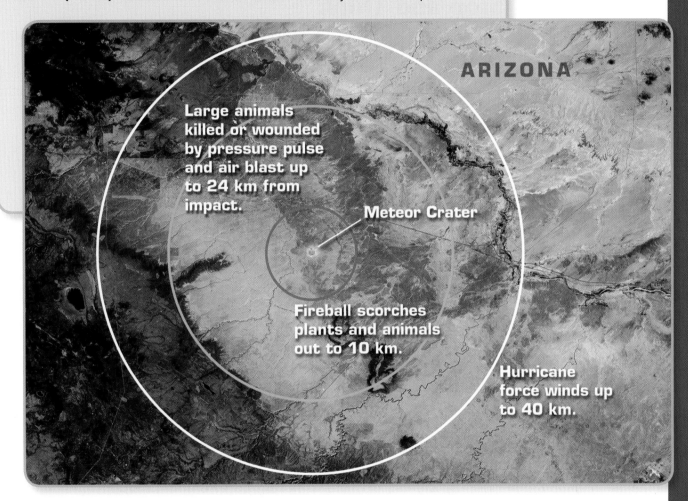

Scanning for Other Craters

Procedure

1. Think about other locations on Earth where craters may be more visible. Use the navigation tools to investigate as many different areas as you have time for. You may ask for help from other students or from your teacher in finding places you could explore.

2. Make a note of any evidence you find that a crater or part of a crater is present. Form a hypothesis for each crater as to whether the crater is an impact crater, a volcanic crater, or was formed by some other natural or artificial process. Record each hypothesis and the evidence that you used to support it.

Stop and Think

1. How many craters did you find on Earth? How do you know they are craters?

2. Where are most of the craters you found? Did you find craters on the land? In the water?

3. Describe the collision of the meteorite with Earth that created Meteor Crater in Arizona.

Reflect

1. What features of the crater did you see in the satellite image of Meteor Crater? Which parts of a crater were difficult to find? Why do you think this is so?

2. Describe the similarities and differences you observe between the image of Meteor Crater and the photographs of different craters on the Moon.

3. Why might it be easier to find craters on Earth by looking at satellite images taken from space rather than pictures taken from the ground?

4. Why do you think there are so many more observable craters on the Moon's surface than on Earth's surface?

Explore Earth's 25 Largest Craters

Meteor Crater in Arizona is large, but it is not one of the largest impact craters on Earth. Your class will use an Earth-imaging program to explore Earth's 25 biggest impact craters and find out where they are located. Each pair of students will explore one crater.

Procedure

1. Type the name of your crater in the *Search* box. When you locate your crater, record the country in which it is found and its longitude and latitude.

2. Make a sketch of your crater on an index card. Label all of the parts and features of the crater that you can observe. Include the **scale** on your drawing so that the sizes of different craters can be compared by using the sketches.

3. Describe any characteristics of the crater, such as the diameter, that you can determine from the satellite image.

4. Use the Internet to find other information about your crater, such as how old it is. Record any relevant or interesting information that you can find about the crater, such as how it was discovered or what is known about the object that formed the crater.

scale: the ratio of the size of a drawing of an object or place to the size of the actual object or place.

geologist: a person who is trained in and works in any of the geologic sciences.

geology (geologic): the study of the planet Earth: the materials of which it is made, the processes that act on these materials, the products formed, and the history of the planet and all its forms since its origin.

astrogeology: the study of the rocks, minerals, and surface features of moons and other planets, applying knowledge of Earth's geology.

Partners in Astronomy

Eugene Shoemaker, trained as a **geologist**, was the first scientist to recognize the possibility that craters on both Earth and on the Moon were caused by meteorite impacts. His 1952 visit to Meteor Crater in Arizona got him interested in the relationship between craters on Earth and on the Moon. He combined his interest in **geology** with astronomy, developing a new field of science known as **astrogeology**. This new area of science extends the study of geology into space.

Communicate

Share Your Findings

Post your index card and indicate your crater's location. As you listen to the description of each crater from the other groups, compare each one to the crater you investigated. Compare the location, diameter, and depth. Think about how the crater is different from yours. Think about how the mass and speed of the objects that caused the craters may compare.

Reflect

1. Describe any patterns you observe in the location of the craters.

2. How do Earth's craters compare to those found on the Moon?

3. Where else do you think craters might be located on Earth? Why would it be difficult to locate some of Earth's craters?

4. Why do you think craters on Earth's surface are more difficult to find than craters on the Moon?

Update the *Project Board*

You have observed craters on the Moon and explored craters on Earth. Now is a good time to update the *Project Board*. Add what you know about the impact of meteorites to the *What are we learning?* column. Be sure to include what you know about craters on the Moon, what you know about craters on Earth, and how those craters are similar and different from each other. Remember to add evidence for each of your entries in the *What are we learning?* column to the *What is our evidence?* column. Also, your observations most likely raised new questions. These questions, or other ideas about which you are unsure, should be added to the *What do we need to investigate?* column.

What's the Point?

Earth's craters are not as easy to locate as craters on the Moon. Lunar craters cover much of the Moon's surface and can easily be seen using a pair of binoculars or a telescope. New technology, such as satellite imaging, can help identify evidence of craters on Earth's surface. However, many fewer craters have been identified on Earth than on the Moon.

1.5 Explore

Why Are Craters More Difficult to Find on Earth Than on the Moon?

You have learned that craters are more common on the Moon than on Earth. You have also noticed that Earth's craters look quite different from the Moon's craters, and discussed some of the reasons why Earth's craters look so different. To understand the nature of collisions with these two bodies, you need to know why craters are more common on the Moon and why Earth's craters look so different from the Moon's craters.

Compare Lunar Craters to Craters on Earth

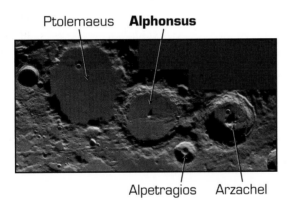

Ptolemaeus **Alphonsus**

Alpetragios   Arzachel

The lunar crater Alphonsus is about 3.9 billion years old. It is still clearly visible on the Moon's surface. Notice that the rim, the evidence of ejecta, and the floor of the crater are all clear. Despite being far older than any crater found on Earth, its features are still intact and quite visible, with no evidence of change.

Earth's Meteor Crater in Arizona, which you observed in the last section, is 50,000 years old. Look at the photographs on the next page. These photographs show some craters on Earth that are older than Meteor Crater, ranging from 300,000 years old to about 212 million years old.

Wolfe Creek Crater

Location: North Central Australia

Diameter: 0.9 km (0.5 mi)

Age: 300,000 years

Description: Partially covered by drifting sand.

Roter Kamm Crater

Location: Namibia

Diameter: 2.5 km (1.5 mi)

Age: Approximately 3.7 million years

Description: Worn down and partially filled with sand.

Manicouagan Crater

Location: Quebec, Canada

Diameter: Approximately 70 km (43 mi)

Age: Approximately 212 million years

Description: Distinct crater shape gone. A ring-shaped depression, filled with water, is still visible.

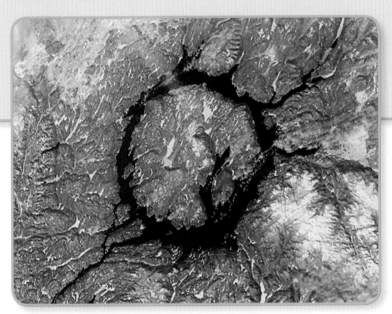

Reflect

1. Many of the craters on the Moon are much older than the craters on Earth. Compare the craters. What features of the craters are clearly visible on the Moon and not visible on Earth?

2. Why do you think the craters on the Moon and craters on Earth look different? What processes on Earth are different from those on the Moon?

3. Why might it be easier to find craters on Earth using satellite images rather than pictures taken from the ground? Think about the images you observed of Roter Kamm as you develop your answer.

weathering: a process in which rocks on Earth's surface are broken down into smaller parts.

erosion: a process in which rocks and rock particles on Earth's surface are carried away by wind or water.

The Covering and Uncovering of Chicxulub Crater

About 65 million years ago, a meteorite collided with Earth at Chicxulub, on the Yucatan Peninsula in southeastern Mexico. The collision resulted in an impact crater about 180 km (112 mi) in diameter. Many scientists believe that this impact was one of the reasons for the extinction of the dinosaurs.

Despite the size of this crater, it was not until the late 1970s that evidence of this crater's existence was found. The crater was not precisely located and identified until 1990. Observe the picture below showing a satellite view of the area.

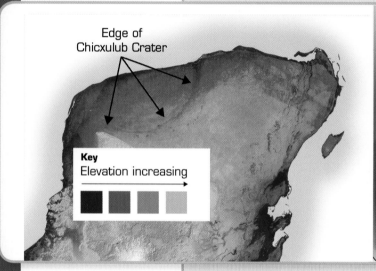

Edge of Chicxulub Crater

Key
Elevation increasing

United States

Gulf of Mexico

Chicxulub Crater

Mexico

Yucatan

As you observe the region in which Chicxulub Crater is located, you might understand why it took so long for it to be discovered. Visible traces of the crater's ring have been broken down into smaller parts in a process called **weathering**. Those rocks and rock parts, which can be as small as sand grains or dust, can be carried away by wind and water in a process called **erosion**. Weathering and erosion are caused by exposure to air, wind, rain, running water, freezing and thawing, and other natural processes. Over a long period of time, many surface features on Earth can be removed or hidden by weathering and erosion.

Most of the craters on Earth's surface are millions of years old. When they were first formed millions, or even hundreds of millions of years ago, these craters may have looked like Meteor Crater or, perhaps, like some of the craters on the Moon. However, Earth's craters are constantly exposed to the processes of erosion and weathering.

Wind can blow particles away from the edges of craters or deposit new particles of rock and soil inside the crater, covering the floor and filling the bowl. Over many years, the shape and size of the crater change. Water is also a powerful agent of erosion. It washes away particles of rock from the sharp crater rims and deposits new materials inside the crater. At times, water may fill craters, making them look like circular lakes.

Many agents of erosion, such as wind and water from precipitation, are the result of weather. Weather takes place in Earth's atmosphere. If Earth did not have an atmosphere, there would be no weather on Earth.

The Moon, unlike Earth, has an atmosphere that is so thin (about one one-hundred trillionth the density of Earth's atmosphere) that it is generally considered to have no atmosphere at all. There is no wind or weather. The Moon also does not have flowing water. Without weather or flowing water, the major processes of weathering do not take place on the Moon.

Not only does the Moon have no weather, the Moon's surface is much older than Earth's. Earth's surface changes much faster than the Moon's surface, in part because Earth's interior is still molten and in motion, while the Moon's interior is not. New surface is formed by volcanoes as Earth's molten interior seeps through cracks. Older parts of the surface are slowly pulled back down into Earth's interior at some regions of the ocean floor. This process slowly turns older rock back into molten material and can remove any trace of a crater. As a result, most of Earth's surface is no older than a few hundred million years. This means that although Earth is billions of years old, most of the surface we see today is no older than a few hundred million years. The oldest craters, too, are no more than a few hundred million years old, and many are younger than that.

Impact craters on the Moon are often larger than those on Earth. Most of the Moon's large craters are billions of years old. At the time these large craters formed, there were probably similar craters on Earth. But Earth's surface is constantly renewed, and this process removes evidence of the large craters that may have existed on Earth billions of years ago.

The Chicxulub crater is still detectable, despite 65 million years of erosion and weathering, thanks to advances in science and technology. With a combination of satellite images, on-site inspections of geological structures, and testing done to samples from a site, scientists can locate and find evidence of impact craters on Earth.

Stop and Think

1. What methods do scientists use to look for evidence of impact craters on Earth?

2. What did this reading tell you about why the impact craters on Earth look so different from the impact craters on the Moon?

3. What other factors do you think make the impact craters on Earth look different from those on the Moon? How do you think these factors might affect the creation of impact craters?

Explain

Use what you have just read, what you know about how impact craters are formed, and what you know about other differences between Earth and the Moon to develop an explanation of why Earth's impact craters look so different from the Moon's impact craters. Work with your group, and use a *Create Your Explanation* page to help you develop your explanation.

Create Your Explanation   1.BBQ.2/2.2.2/2.BBQ.3

Name:_____   Date:_____

Use this page to explain the lesson of your recent investigations.

Write a brief summary of the results from your investigation. You will use this summary to help you write your explanation.

Claim—a statement of what you understand or a conclusion that you have reached from an investigation or a set of investigations.

Evidence—data collected during investigations and trends in that data.

Science knowledge—knowledge about how things work. You may have learned this through reading, talking to an expert, discussion, or other experiences.

Write your explanation using your **Claim, Evidence** and **Science knowledge** from above.

© It's About Time

Begin by developing a claim. Your claim will be a statement about the similarities and differences between the impact craters on Earth and on the Moon.

Then record evidence that supports your claim. Your evidence might come from the experiments the class ran earlier in the Unit. It also might come from your observations of the satellite images, or it might come from the photographs you have been examining.

Science knowledge can come from what you have been reading. You also gained science knowledge when you used the Internet to look up information about Earth's impact craters in *Section 1.4.*

After recording your claim, evidence, and science knowledge, develop an explanation statement that pulls together your claim with your evidence and science knowledge. A good explanation will help somebody know what you think has been happening on Earth and on the Moon that makes the craters on the two bodies look so different from each other.

Communicate

Share Your Explanation

When everyone is finished, share your explanation with the class. When it is your group's turn, begin by presenting your claim. Then present your evidence and science knowledge. After that, present your explanation statement.

As each group shares their explanation, listen carefully for how each explanation is similar to yours or different from yours. Record any differences you notice and any disagreements you have so you will remember them after all of the explanations have been presented.

After all of the explanations have been presented, discuss their strengths and weaknesses. As a class, select or develop a claim and explanation that everyone thinks best explains the difference in craters on Earth and on the Moon.

Reflect

To answer the questions below, use the explanation the class has developed. Be prepared to share your answers with the class.

1. What changes would you expect to observe in Meteor Crater if you could come back and look at it a million years from now?

2. Which of the craters examined by your class would Meteor Crater be most like in a million years?

3. Another difference between Earth and the Moon is that Earth has water on its surface. How do you think the structure of a crater would change if a meteorite struck water instead of striking land?

4. Why do you think there are fewer impact craters on Earth than on the Moon?

5. Why do you think impact craters on the Moon are larger than impact craters on Earth?

What's the Point?

Over time, erosion and weathering by wind, water, and other natural processes, create large changes in the craters formed on Earth. The Moon has no wind or flowing water, so erosion and weathering do not affect craters on the Moon as they do on Earth. The Moon's surface is also much older than Earth's, so the craters on the Moon are much older than craters on Earth. The Moon's craters are also larger than Earth's impact craters. Billions of years ago, when large craters formed on the Moon, similar craters formed on Earth. As Earth's surface is renewed, evidence of the older craters is completely erased.

The first footprints on the Moon, made by Apollo 11 astronauts Neil Armstrong and Buzz Aldrin, will be there for a million years. There is no erosion or weathering by wind or water to affect them.

1.6 Explore

What Happens When a Meteorite Hits Earth?

From Meteoroid to Meteor to Meteorite

The solar system is full of debris. Besides planets, moons, and the Sun, our solar system contains many smaller bodies that you will learn about in the next section. A **meteoroid** is any one of these bodies that travels through the solar system with the potential to collide with Earth.

Most objects in the solar system travel through space very quickly. For example, Earth revolves around the Sun at a speed of about 30 kilometers per second. Other objects, such as meteoroids, travel at similar speeds, or even faster. You can imagine that if two objects moving at these speeds collide, the impact will be quite violent.

The first thing that happens to a meteoroid as it approaches Earth is that it falls under the influence of Earth's gravity. Earth's gravity pulls objects toward Earth's center. As a meteoroid approaches Earth, gravity will alter its path, causing the meteoroid to bend toward Earth's surface. Most meteoroids can pass by Earth with their motion deflected slightly by gravity, but without ever having a collision. Other meteoroids strike Earth's atmosphere.

When a meteoroid comes within 50 kilometers of Earth's surface, it is well within Earth's atmosphere. The meteoroid collides with air particles in Earth's atmosphere. However, the meteoroid is moving so quickly that it pushes together the air particles in front of it. This compressed air heats up and vaporizes layers of the meteoroid. The heat is so intense that it changes the top layers of the solid meteoroid into gas. The meteoroid heats up to the point that it begins to glow, and the hot gases escaping from the meteoroid also create a bright stream of light. The object is now clearly visible from Earth's surface, and it is now called a **meteor**. The flashes of light are often called shooting stars or falling stars, but these are not stars at all.

meteoroid: a small-solar system body that has the potential to become a meteor.

meteor: an object that enters Earth's atmosphere with such speed that it glows.

Meteor showers are events during which many meteors appear in the same part of the sky during the same night.

ASTRONOMY

Most meteors completely break apart and burn up in Earth's atmosphere before they have time to collide with Earth's surface. The original meteoroid may have been too small, or it may have entered the atmosphere at a small angle, or it may have been made of materials that break apart or vaporize easily. Only a few meteors survive the trip and strike Earth. These objects are the ones called meteorites.

Earth's atmosphere slows down a meteorite, but after passing through Earth's atmosphere, meteorites are still often traveling at great speeds when they impact Earth's surface. The crater formed is much larger than the meteorite. Remember, the object that formed the 1.3-km Meteor Crater was only 50 m wide.

In many cases, a meteorite is destroyed by its impact. Scientists are forced to look for fragments of the meteorite or other indicators of the original object. One thing scientists look for are small spheres of meteoritic iron among the ejecta around the rim of a crater. Many meteoroids contain significant quantities of iron, so this metal shows up in the fragments of meteorites.

Stop and Think

1. Why are impacts between meteorites and Earth so violent?

2. If Earth's gravity were stronger, what effect would you expect this to have on meteoroids passing by Earth? On meteorites that strike Earth?

3. How does Earth's atmosphere affect the motion of a meteoroid?

4. Why do some meteoroids that are traveling toward Earth never hit Earth's surface?

5. Why do meteors glow?

Observe

Meteors travel through the atmosphere so fast that they glow. In the video, you will see a fire syringe used to simulate a meteor traveling through the sky. The plunger will act like the meteoroid, compressing air in its path. As the plunger is pushed down quickly, more pressure will build up in the cylinder. This will create intense heat at the bottom of a cylinder.

Reflect

1. What did you observe happen to the tissue paper inside the cylinder?

2. Do you think the gas is the source of the glow in the syringe, or the tissue paper? Why? What does this tell you about the reason(s) a meteor glows?

3. If a meteor burns up before it reaches the ground, is there any evidence that a collision took place? Why or why not?

Update the *Project Board*

Record what you now know about what happens when meteoroids hit Earth and the Moon in the *What are we learning?* column of the *Project Board*. Be sure to include what you know about how and why impact craters on Earth and on the Moon are different from each other. As always, make sure you include supporting evidence for anything added to this column in the *What is our evidence?* column. Your evidence may come from what you have read, your experiments, and the demonstration.

You now have a lot of experience thinking about what happens when meteoroids strike Earth or the Moon. You may be wondering about where these objects come from and what different types of objects exist, and whether these different objects can strike Earth or the Moon. Can these solar system objects strike other planets? Add these questions and any others you have to the *Project Board* in the *What do we need to investigate?* column.

What's the Point?

Earth's atmosphere makes it difficult for meteoroids to get all the way to Earth without burning up. Air particles in the atmosphere are compressed by the object. This creates enough heat to vaporize an object before it reaches Earth's surface. The Moon has no atmosphere. Therefore, meteoroids meet no resistance as they speed toward the Moon, so they do not vaporize. Only the larger and faster-moving objects are able to pass through Earth's atmosphere and become meteorites by striking the surface. For this reason, more meteoroids hit the Moon than Earth, even though Earth is so much larger than the Moon.

1.7 Read

What Other Evidence Exists of Past Collisions in our Solar System?

So far, you have learned about evidence of collisions on Earth and the Moon, and you have learned some things about what happens when these collisions occur. You can learn even more about potential collisions between solar-system objects by looking at collisions in other parts of the solar system. The solar system contains many different types of objects, some of which could be dangerous to Earth, and some of which are not. Other solar-system bodies also contain evidence of past collisions. In this section, you will get an introduction to the solar system and learn about one collision that scientists were actually able to observe from Earth.

dwarf planet: a round solar-system body that is smaller than a planet.

asteroid belt: a region of the solar system between Mars and Jupiter in which most asteroids are located.

Planets and Planet-like Objects

To understand the collisions that caused the impact craters on Earth and the Moon, you need to know more about the types of objects that are in the solar system. You already know that the solar system includes the Sun, eight planets, and their moons.

The eight planets, in order from closest to the Sun to farthest away, are Mercury, Venus, Earth, Mars, Jupiter, Saturn, Uranus, and Neptune.

The solar system also includes **dwarf planets**. Dwarf planets are planet-like objects that are not large enough to be considered planets. The smallest planet, Mercury, is about 2,440 km (1516 mi) in diameter, so all dwarf planets are smaller than Mercury. Dwarf planets are round, like planets. However, planets travel in nearly circular paths around the Sun, with no other objects traveling in the same circle. Dwarf planets may travel in oval orbits, or they may travel in a circular path around the Sun, like planets.

As of 2009, five dwarf planets were known: Ceres, Pluto, Eris, Makemake, and Haumea. Ceres, the smallest dwarf planet, is located in the **asteroid belt** between Mars and Jupiter. Pluto was classified as a planet between 1930, the year of its discovery, and 2006. It is now considered a dwarf planet because of its size and oval path around the Sun. Eris, Makemake, and Haumea are all located much farther away than Neptune from the Sun and have oval paths around the Sun. They were not even identified until 2004 and 2005, so perhaps many more dwarf planets are still awaiting investigation.

In addition to the eight planets, scientists have created the category of dwarf planets. Pictured in this artist's illustration are three dwarf planets: Ceres, Pluto, and Eris. Not to scale—it illustrates the relative size of the planets and the dwarf planets in our solar system.

Small Solar-System Bodies

Besides planets and dwarf planets, other smaller objects also revolve around the Sun. Objects in the solar system that revolve around the Sun but are not large enough to be called dwarf planets are called *small solar-system bodies.*

Bodies in the solar system are classified by the International Astronomical Union (IAU), a group of astronomers recognized as the worldwide authority in astronomy. One of the duties of IAU is to establish names for all of the objects scientists discover. Another duty is to give standard meanings to

asteroid: a rocky or metallic solar-system body that revolves around the Sun, between 10 m (33 ft) and about 500 km (310 mi) in diameter.

comet: a small, icy solar-system body that revolves around the Sun and forms a tail as it gets closer to the Sun.

coma: the cloud of gas and dust that forms around a comet as parts of the comet vaporize.

words to allow easier communication between astronomers. Some of the other objects that you need to know about to answer the *Big Question* are **asteroids** and **comets**.

Asteroids are irregularly shaped rocks that revolve around the Sun but are too small to be considered planets or dwarf planets. Over one million asteroids revolve around the Sun in a group located between Mars and Jupiter. This region is called the asteroid belt. However, a few asteroids can also be found in other parts of the solar system. An object is generally not considered an asteroid unless it is larger than 10 m (32 ft) across. The largest asteroids are 500 km (311 mi) across.

Comets are another important type of small solar-system body. Comets are small icy objects, usually less than 10 km (6 mi) across. They are made up of mostly ice and dust. Although comets are about the same size as some asteroids, they are less massive, because they are made of ice instead of rock and iron. Comets are often referred to as "dirty snowballs," because dust and ice are their main ingredients.

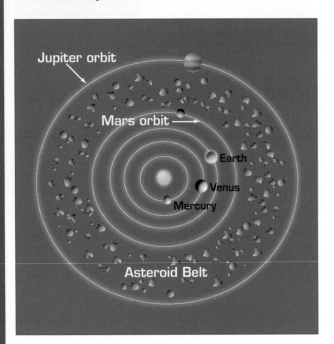

This illustration of the asteroid belt shows the location of one million asteroids. Not to scale.

Most of the time, comets are found far out in the solar system. Sometimes, they move in closer to the Sun. As they approach the Sun, some of the surface ice starts to melt and vaporize, producing a large cloud called a **coma**. Comas can reach up to 2.4 million km (1.5 million mi) in diameter! Light and charged particles flowing from the Sun push the gas and dust around the comet into a long, curved tail.

The gas and dust that form the comet's tail are left behind as the comet continues in its orbit. Later, Earth's motion in the solar system might take it through this same debris trail. The debris collides with Earth's atmosphere, but it burns up long before any of it reaches the ground. Because Earth collides with many such particles at the same time, the result is sometimes a spectacular display of meteors called a meteor shower.

Earth can also pass directly through the tail of a comet. The result is a more spectacular meteor shower, but as long as the body of the comet misses Earth, no damage will occur.

Halley's Comet, the famous comet named after English astronomer Edmund Halley, can be viewed from Earth every 76 years. Halley's Comet, like many others, has a predictable pattern of movement. It made its last close approach to the Sun on February 9, 1986, and it will next streak by the Sun on July 28, 2061.

Carolyn Shoemaker: Comet hunter.

All comets are named after the person or people who discovered them. Carolyn Shoemaker is the most accomplished comet hunter alive. She has found more than 800 asteroids and 32 comets. Carolyn Shoemaker, like all comet hunters, is successful because she patiently observes changes in the sky, using a telescope and numerous slides taken of space objects.

Comets consist mainly of ice and dust. The comet's large cloud, called the coma, is surface ice that starts to melt and vaporize as the comet approaches the Sun.

Watching a Collision in the Solar System

In the summer of 1994, pieces of a large comet crashed into Jupiter. Pictures of this remarkable event appeared throughout the media.

About a year before the collision, in March 1993, Carolyn Shoemaker, her husband Eugene, and David Levy had discovered that comet. Using a telescope, the three spotted the comet and watched as it passed Jupiter. The comet had passed very close to Jupiter, and the gravity of Jupiter was strong enough to break it into 21 large pieces. This made the comet appear as a string of pearls.

Comet Shoemaker-Levy 9 collided with Jupiter in many pieces.

The scientists shared their findings with others. Scientists were able to predict that the next time the comet came close to Jupiter, it would actually collide with Jupiter. They were right. Beginning in July 1994, the world watched as piece after piece of the comet, named Shoemaker-Levy 9, smashed into Jupiter's atmosphere.

Jupiter's surface is not rocky like that of Earth. Jupiter's surface is composed of liquid hydrogen and helium under intense pressure. So, the result of a collision with Jupiter is much different from one on Earth.

When the first fragment of Shoemaker-Levy 9 hit Jupiter, its impact released as much energy as 225,000 million tons of dynamite and produced a plume of gas and debris that rose 1000 km (621 mi) above the planet's cloud layers. The impact completely destroyed the fragment, leaving small particles, similar to dust. Each impact of the broken comet pieces also formed a dark spot on Jupiter. These large spots were made of debris from the comet. Several impact sites were about half the diameter of Earth.

As the remaining fragments of the comet hit Jupiter, more dark spots appeared from the impacts. Some fragments did not leave any marks on Jupiter, perhaps because of their small size. Although they remained visible for several weeks after the collision, the dark spots eventually disappeared.

Today there is no evidence of the Shoemaker-Levy 9 comet colliding with Jupiter in 1994.

Stop and Think

1. When Shoemaker-Levy 9 hit Jupiter, the impacts caused many changes. Describe the impacts and the changes.

2. The impact of the comet and Jupiter was the first to be predicted by scientists. Why do you think impacts with Jupiter may not have been observed or recorded before? What do you think happened to the evidence of the collisions?

3. How was the impact with Jupiter different from impacts that have occurred on Earth or the Moon?

4. At the end of *Section 1.2,* you were shown a photo of a string of craters on one of the moons of Jupiter. How does what you learned about the Shoemaker-Levy 9 comet change your understanding of how those craters formed?

Reflect

Throughout this Unit, you will read more about the solar system. You just read about some of the objects in the solar system. However, the solar system is more than a collection of objects. It is a system that is constantly in motion, with its different parts interacting through collisions, gravity, and radiation.

By the end of this Unit, you will be able to write a thorough description of how the solar system works. You will be able to explain how it was formed, where the different parts come from, and how they interact with one another.

You will now begin to record what you are learning about the solar system. Later, you will use this information to develop your explanations.
Use the questions that follow to help you record your knowledge on a
Solar System page.

Solar System	1.7.1/2.BBQ.2

Name: _____   Date: _____

Solar System Object	What characteristics does this object have?	How does this object move?
The Sun		
The Moon		
Inner Planets (Mercury, Venus, Earth, Mars)		
Outer planets (Jupiter, Saturn, Uranus, Neptune)		
Dwarf planets		
Asteroids, comets, meteoroids		
Other small solar-system bodies		

© It's About Time

1. Use what you have learned in this section and anything you have learned previously to start filling out a *Solar System* page. For each type of object in the solar system that you have read about in this Unit, list its characteristics, and then describe its motion. Do not worry if there are rows or columns on the page that you do not understand. You can skip those and return to them later in the Unit.

2. After you have finished working on your *Solar System* page, get together with your group to discuss your page. Use your discussion to add to or revise what you have written. Notice any disagreements you have with other group members.

3. With your group, identify what else you need to learn about the solar system to be able to answer the *Big Question*.

Update the *Project Board*

Add what you now know about the solar system to the *What have we learned?* column of the *Project Board*. Don't forget to add evidence to the *What is our evidence?* column. You have generated questions about the solar system. Add those to the *What do we need to investigate?* column of the *Project Board*. Make sure your personal *Project Board* matches the class Project Board.

What's the Point?

The solar system consists of eight planets and their moons, as well as a number of dwarf planets and other small solar-system bodies. These bodies include asteroids, comets, and meteoroids. All of the bodies in the solar system can be involved in collisions. In one spectacular collision in 1994, scientists watched a comet as it broke apart and then collided with the planet Jupiter.

Learning Set 1

Back to the Big Question

How can you know if objects in space will collide?

The study of craters has provided scientists with a lot of information about when objects have collided and the sizes of the objects. Astrogeologists are one group of scientists who study different solar-system objects. By continuing to study these objects, scientists have an understanding of collisions that occurred in the past. They are also beginning to understand the changes that could happen on Earth as a result of collisions, what caused the collisions, and how often they occur.

The *Big Question* for the Unit is *How can you know if objects in space will collide?* Understanding the evidence of collisions can help you begin to answer this question. You will conclude this Unit by writing a report that answers the question. This *Learning Set* discussed the question, *Have objects in the solar system collided?* So far, you have looked at evidence of collisions on Earth, the Moon, and Jupiter. You have also been introduced to some of the objects in the solar system that might collide with one another. Now you will focus on one specific object and predict what would happen if it collided with Earth.

Explore

Each group will use the Internet and other resources to gather information about one of the four solar-system objects described on the next page. You will be assigned an object your group will study. As you gather the information, you should remember that you are responsible for teaching other groups about your solar-system object. Based on what you find, you will answer two questions: *What would happen if this object collided with Earth?* and *Is it likely that this object will collide with Earth in the next 30 years?*

Halley's Comet

Widespread news coverage of the close passage of Halley's Comet occurred in the days before the comet's closest approach, in May of 1910. Some people feared a potential collision or terrible results as Earth passed through the comet's tail.

The Great Daylight Fireball of 1972

Around 2:30 in the afternoon on August 10, 1972, a streak of fire appeared in the sky above Utah. This turned out to be the first scientifically observed "Earth-grazing" meteoroid. It passed close enough to Earth that it went through Earth's atmosphere, becoming a glowing meteor. But instead of colliding with Earth, it flew past it.

Asteroid 1999 AN10

The asteroid 1999 AN10 was one of the first asteroids discovered by the Lincoln Near-Earth Asteroid Research (LINEAR) program. In the year 2027, it will pass within 390,000 kilometers of Earth, which is similar to the average distance of the Moon from Earth.

Asteroid 433 Eros

Eros was the first near-Earth asteroid discovered. On February 12, 2001, it became the first object in the solar system other than a planet or a moon to have a probe from Earth land on it. The asteroid has an oblong shape.

Procedure

1. Using available resources, gather the following information about the solar-system object assigned to your group.

   • size

   • mass

   • composition

   • distance from the Sun (give a range if this distance varies)

   • how and when the object was discovered

   • any other interesting information

2. Determine among your group members what you think would happen if your solar-system object were to collide with Earth. List your ideas and the supporting evidence. Your evidence is the information you have gathered about your solar-system object and the evidence from past collisions that you have studied in this *Learning Set*.

3. Determine among your group members whether you think your object is likely to collide with Earth in the next 30 years. List your ideas and the supporting evidence.

4. Prepare a poster to share with the class. Be sure to include a picture of your solar-system object, the information you gathered, and your answers to the two questions. Make sure you include the evidence used for your answers. Be prepared to explain how your group reached your conclusions and why.

Communicate

Investigation Expo

When you have finished your information gathering and discussions and prepared your poster, you will share what you learned with the class in an *Investigation Expo*. In this *Expo*, each group will take turns presenting their information and conclusions to the class. So that others will be able to learn from your work and use your information, you must clearly present the information on your poster.

While you are listening to the presentations of other groups, be ready to ask questions so that you can better understand the groups' conclusions. Some questions you might want to ask include these:

- What type of solar-system object is your object: a comet, an asteroid, or something else?

- What evidence of past collisions with similar objects helped you predict what might happen if your object collided with Earth?

- What was the most important evidence used to reach your conclusion about the likelihood of a collision?

Reflect

Now that you have listened to all the presentations in your class, you need to start thinking about preparing your report that answers the *Big Question: How can you know if objects in space will collide?* The first step in writing a good report is organizing all of the information you have. Right now, you don't have enough information to write a complete report, but you can still get started with organizing it.

Use the *Big Question* page to list what you have learned so far about the objects in the solar system. Use the first column to record the objects or types of objects that you think your report should include. It will help if you can group objects together. For example, instead of listing different comets separately, you can list comets as a type of object, and make notes on individual comets in the last three columns as needed.

	Big Question	1.BBQ.1/2.BBQ.2
Name: _____		Date: _____

How Can You Know if Objects in Space Will Collide?

Type of Object	Evidence of Past Collisions	Chance of Future Collisions	What Would Happen?

© It's About Time

Use the last three columns to record information that would be useful for your report. The *Evidence of Past Collisions* column should list any evidence that these objects have collided with other space objects in the past. The *Chance of Future Collisions* column should list any evidence that these objects could collide with other space objects in the future. The *What Would Happen?* column should list your ideas on what would happen if a collision occurred and what could be done to prevent such a collision.

Fill out the chart as best you can. You can discuss your ideas with other members in your group. Recall what you learned from the class presentations and use that information in your chart.

Explain

It is time to make your first explanation of how you can tell if space objects will collide. For this explanation, you will consider two space objects. Your teacher will tell you the first object, and the second object will be Earth. Use a *Create Your Explanation* page to help you. Remember that a good explanation has several parts to it:

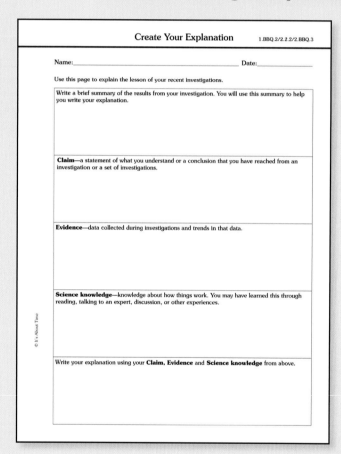

- **your claim:** a statement of what you understand or a conclusion you have reached

- **your evidence:** data collected from investigations that support your claim

- **your science knowledge:** knowledge about how things work that supports your claim

- **your explanation:** a logical statement connecting your evidence and science knowledge to your claim in a way that can convince someone that your claim is valid. Good explanations tell what is happening that makes the claim valid.

Your claim will be your clearest, most accurate statement about how scientists can know whether the space objects will collide. Your evidence comes from your investigations into craters, the information you have gathered on a space object, and your experience with collisions.

Your science knowledge comes from your reading. Use what you have learned so far to make the best explanation you can right now. It may be easier to express your explanation by attaching phrases to sketches than to simply use words. Feel free to combine sketches and words in your explanation. You will have a chance later in the Unit to revise your explanation.

Communicate

Share Your Explanation

Share your group's explanation with the rest of the class. As you are listening to the explanations of other groups, look for anything they have to say about determining whether two space objects will collide that you did not include in your explanation.

Reflect

With your group, answer the following questions.

1. How trustworthy and complete do you think your explanation is?

2. What else do you need to investigate and learn to improve your explanation of how scientists can know if two space objects will collide?

Update the *Project Board*

It is now time to update the *Project Board* with information about different solar-system objects. Think about what is most important about each solar-system object you learned about. Consider the similarities and differences among these objects and include this information in the *What are we learning?* column. Support your learning with evidence from your research or reading. Record this evidence in the *What is our evidence?* column.

Although you are learning about many different objects in the solar system, there may still be some things you think you know but are not quite sure about. You should record these ideas in the *What do we think we know?* column. In the *Investigation Expo,* you listened to presentations about what would happen if some of these objects hit Earth. The information in those presentations will be useful for your report. Add this information to the *What does this mean for the challenge or question?* column.

You may also have realized that you need to learn more about the objects in the solar system to determine if collisions will occur. For example, you need to understand how objects in the solar system move in relation to one another. You also need to understand how gravity works. Add these and any other questions to the *What do we need to learn?* column of the *Project Board.*

Learning Set 2

How Do Earth, the Moon, and the Sun Move Through Space?

Using a telescope, you can see most of the big objects in our solar system from right where you are on Earth. The one big solar-system object you cannot see in the sky is Earth itself. Only the few people who have traveled in space have seen Earth from a different viewpoint. So, how can you find out about where objects in the solar system are located? And what is Earth's place in the solar system?

In *Learning Set 1,* you learned about some solar-system objects that have collided with other solar-system bodies, including Earth. You can tell from the size of the craters formed that the impacting objects must have been moving at great speeds. But remember that Earth is also moving through the solar system. So, to accurately predict whether an object in space will collide with another object, you need to know where the object is, how it is moving, where the other object is, and how that object is moving.

People on Earth have always looked up at the sky and wondered about what they saw. The two most noticeable objects are the Sun and the Moon. From your place here on Earth, you have observed the Moon, our closest neighbor. Over a certain period of time, you may have noticed how the Moon's appearance changes from day to day. You may have observed patterns in these changes and questioned why they occur. Ancient astronomers did the same thing. Over time, they realized that the movements of the Sun and the Moon are predictable.

The Moon is often visible during daylight hours.

In this *Learning Set,* you will do something similar to what ancient astronomers did. You will observe patterns in the movements of the Moon and Sun. Then, based on what you observe, you will do your best to determine how the Sun, Moon, and Earth move through space. This will prepare you to learn about movements of other objects in the solar system. You will need to know all of this to answer the *Big Question.*

2.1 Understand the Question

Think About How You Can Find Out About the Motions of Earth, the Moon, and the Sun

You know that the Sun rises in the east and sets in the west. This movement is predictable and has been observed for hundreds of thousands of years. You have probably learned that the spinning of Earth causes this *apparent movement* of the Sun across the sky. *Apparent movement* refers to what the movement of objects in space looks like to an observer on Earth. However, because Earth is also moving, the apparent movement you observe is not necessarily the same as the actual movement of those objects. People have not always known that Earth is spinning. Until 1850, nobody could prove that Earth rotates. Then the French scientist Jean Foucault designed an experiment with a large pendulum swinging in a circle of pegs.

The pendulum shifted slowly and knocked down pegs throughout the day. Because of the way he had set up the experiment, only a rotating movement of Earth could have caused the pendulum to knock down the pegs. That was the first time a scientist had provided evidence that Earth is rotating.

Although Foucault's pendulum seemed to swing back and forth in one line, because of the rotating movement of Earth, it changed position and, throughout the day, it knocked down many pegs.

Project-Based Inquiry Science

You learned in *Learning Set 1* that Earth revolves around the Sun. It is easy to confuse the term rotation with the term *revolution*. Rotation refers to spinning. Revolution refers to moving around another object. It may help to remember that an object can spin in place, like a rotating top. If an object is revolving, it cannot stay in place as it moves around another object. And of course, an object can rotate and revolve at the same time, as Earth does.

Knowing where objects are located in the solar system requires knowing how they are moving. That was hard for astronomers to determine. For the next few days, you are going to imagine that you know absolutely nothing about the movement of Earth. You are going to observe the apparent motion of the Sun across the sky, experiencing what it was like for early scientists who relied on observations to figure out how Earth and other objects in the sky move in relation to one another. You will be using shadows to observe the apparent motion of the Sun across the sky. Then you will use your observations to try to explain why the length and direction of a shadow changes throughout the day.

sundial: a device that measures time using shadows cast by an object that blocks the Sun's light.

You will do this by examining the shadows made by a **sundial**. A sundial is a device that measures time using the shadows the Sun makes. The simplest type of sundial is a stick in the ground with a flat surface around it on all sides. As far back as 3500 B.C.E., people realized that one could measure how time passed by looking at the shadows of a sundial.

Get Started

You will be observing images that show how a sundial's shadow changes over the course of a day. You will observe how the position of the Sun in the sky relates to the shadows. You will then consider how changes in the shadows relate to the apparent motion of the Sun. You will organize your observations on a *Sundial Patterns* page.

Your *Sundial Patterns* page has two parts. The bottom space is for recording the length and direction of each shadow you observe. The upper space is for recording the position of the Sun in the sky that corresponds to each shadow.

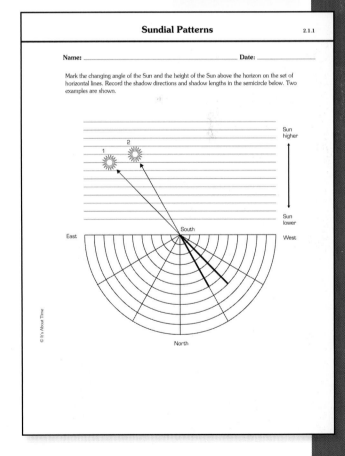

Procedure: The Apparent Motion of the Sun

1. With your group, look at the sequence of images of the shadows on a sundial. These images show the shadows cast by the simplest form of a sundial—a stick fixed vertically in the ground. For each image, notice where the Sun is and where the shadow is. Notice that the Sun is always on the opposite side of the sundial from the shadow. Notice how the height of the Sun corresponds to the length of the shadow.

2. Look at the *Sundial Patterns* page with your group. The shadows for Images #1 and #2 have been drawn for you. The position of the Sun in the sky when it makes those shadows has also been sketched and labeled.

3. Using the shadows marked for Images #1 and #2 to guide you, mark and label the shadows for Images #3, #4, #5, #6, and #7. You are only looking for patterns, so you do not need to make the drawings exact.

4. Using the Sun's positions marked for Images #1 and #2 to guide you, mark and label the position of the Sun in the sky for Images #3, #4, #5, #6, and #7. You do not need to make the drawings exact.

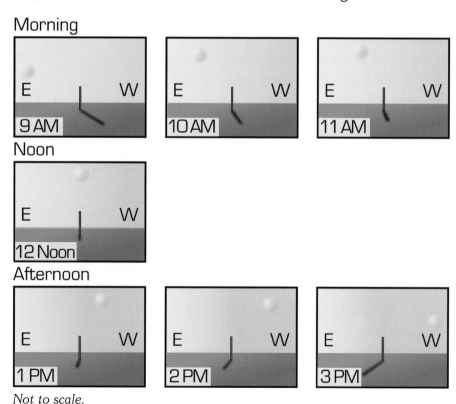

Morning

9 AM 10 AM 11 AM

Noon

12 Noon

Afternoon

1 PM 2 PM 3 PM

Not to scale.

Analyze Your Data

1. Describe any patterns you can observe in the shadows throughout the day.

2. Describe any patterns you can observe in the position of the Sun throughout the day.

3. Why do you think the length of the shadow changes throughout the day?

4. How do the sundial shadows record the apparent movement of the Sun across the sky?

5. What do you know about shadows that helped you answer these questions?

Reflect

1. What do you think the sundial shadows would look like if images were produced for two days in a row?

2. What would you tell people about the apparent motion of the Sun across the sky? How would you support what you tell them with your observations?

How a Sundial Works

Sundials are tools developed by ancient civilizations for measuring time. A sundial uses positions of the Sun throughout the day to measure time. As Earth rotates, the position of the Sun appears to change. As the position of the Sun changes throughout the day, so does the position of the shadows it makes.

Shadows occur because light travels in a straight line. If an object blocks the path of some rays of sunlight, the area on the ground directly behind the object appears darker because less light reaches it. The darker area is the object's shadow. A stick casts the shortest shadow on the ground when the Sun is at its highest point in the sky. You can see in the diagram on the next page that when the Sun is lower in the sky, the shadow is longer because the stick blocks more of the ground from receiving direct sunlight. Light from the Sun casts the longest shadows at sunrise and sunset, when the Sun is lowest in the sky.

gnomon: the object on a sundial blocking direct light from the Sun and casting a shadow.

The pointer on a sundial, called a **gnomon**, is the object blocking direct light from the Sun. It creates shadows that fall on the sundial face, which has lines marked to show the hours. As the Sun appears to move across the sky, the gnomon's shadow moves across the hour lines, measuring the time.

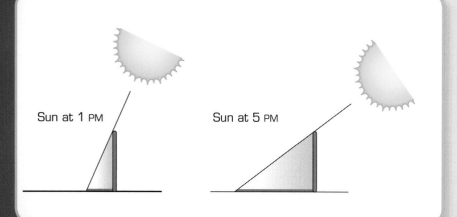

Sun at 1 PM   Sun at 5 PM

The Sun rises in the east and sets in the west. A shadow points away from the Sun, so a shadow cast by the Sun at sunrise points west. At noon, the shadow points north. At sunset, the shadow points east. The direction of this pattern on the sundial face is clockwise, from west to north to east. The hands of a clock follow this pattern. The hour hand moves in the same direction as the shadow on a sundial.

Any tall object, including this child and the Sundial Bridge in California, can cast a shadow on a surface to measure time.

Reflect

1. How could you use a vertical stick to create a sundial? What do you think you would need to know to tell the correct time using the shadow of the stick?

2. Why do you think sundials are not used as time-keeping instruments today?

3. Where would the Sun have to be for a vertical stick to cast no visible shadow on a sunny day?

4. How would you explain to someone why the Sun seems to move throughout the day when observed from Earth?

5. What else do you need to know to give a more complete explanation about where the Sun is and why it seems to move across the sky?

6. Think about how the Sun's apparent movement makes it *seem* as if the Sun goes around Earth. Yet you know that the Sun is at the center of the solar system and that Earth revolves about the Sun. What does that tell you about what else you need to know to determine the location and movement of objects in the solar system?

Update the *Project Board*

In the *What do we think we know?* column of the *Project Board*, record what you think you know about how to identify the location and motion of objects as seen from Earth. In the *What are we learning?* column of the *Project Board,* record the questions the class has generated. Update your own *Project Board* during the class discussion.

What's the Point?

You have observed that the Sun's position in the sky changes throughout the day. Shadows cast by an object that blocks sunlight change from long in the morning to short at midday to long in the afternoon. The direction of this pattern of shadows is from west to north to east. Since a shadow points in the direction opposite the Sun's position, you know that the direction of the Sun's apparent path across the sky is from east to west. Sundials are used to measure time using the position of a gnomon's shadow as it crosses hour lines on the face of the sundial.

You know Earth is actually revolving around the Sun, so it might be difficult for you to figure out how the Sun could look like it is moving. It was also difficult for scientists to figure that out. Even after scientists knew Earth was revolving around the Sun, it was hundreds of years before they proved that Earth rotates. Yet understanding Earth's movements and the movements of other space objects are essential for predicting whether an object in space will collide with Earth. In the rest of the *Learning Set,* you will be answering your questions about the locations and movements of the Sun, Moon, and Earth. Then, in later *Learning Sets,* you will know how to determine the location and movement of other space objects.

In this composite picture of our solar system are the eight planets and four of Jupiter's largest moons, taken as if from Earth's moon.

2.2 Model

Make a Model of the Apparent Motion of the Sun

You observed shadows to record the apparent motion of the Sun across the sky during the day. However, it was hard to know what the pattern of the shadows made by the sundial illustrated about the Sun's actual motion or the location of the Sun and Earth in the solar system. In this section, you will use simple materials to make a model to help you understand the Sun's movement across the sky and the location of the Sun in relation to Earth.

In the model, you will use a flashlight to represent the Sun. You will use a globe to represent Earth. The globe spins on an **axis**, which is a line through the globe that doesn't move as the globe spins. You will manipulate the globe and flashlight until your model can make the same shadows that you observed in the images.

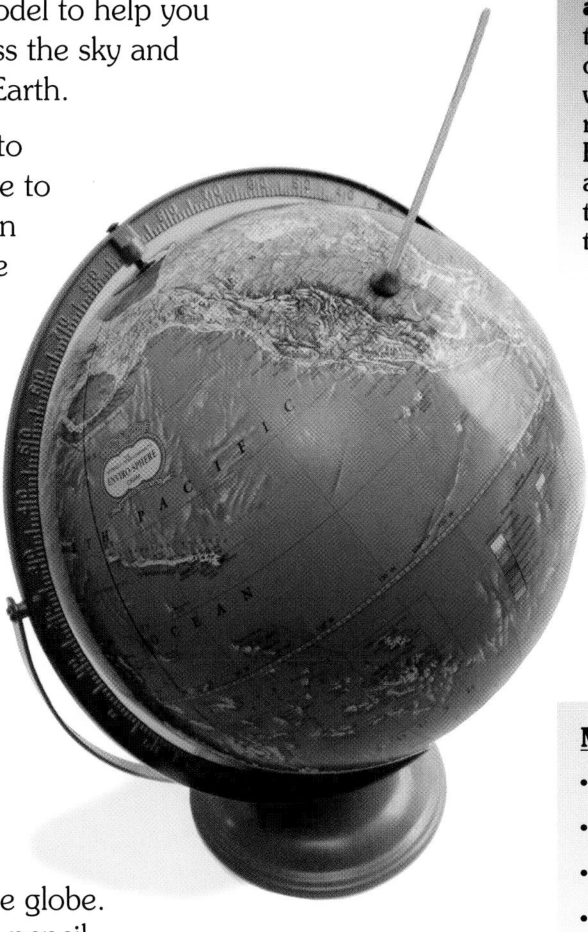

axis: a line through the center of a body, around which the body rotates, or spins; Earth's imaginary axis passes through the North Pole and the South Pole.

Investigation 1: Make a Model that Shows Changes in the Shadow's Direction

Procedure

1. Find the area where you live on the globe. Use the clay to securely attach the pencil to that location. The pencil should be pointed directly away from the center of the globe.

Materials
- short pencil
- clay
- flashlight
- Earth globe mounted on an axis

ASTRONOMY

2. Use the flashlight to represent the Sun and the pencil attached to the globe to represent the gnomon of a sundial. Move the flashlight and/or the globe so that the changes in the *direction* the shadow is pointing are the same as they were on the sundial. Do not worry yet about making sure the shadows are the right length.

   (Hint: To find directions, first find north. You know where the North Pole is on the globe. That should help you.)

3. Record a description of the way the direction of the shadows changed. Then record a description of what you did to the globe and the flashlight to simulate the pattern of shadow directions on a sundial. Write several sentences and sketch what you did.

Investigation 2: Make a Model to Show Changes in the Shadow's Length

Procedure

1. Use the same setup. The pencil should be attached to the globe at your location on Earth. It should point straight up from the center of the globe. The flashlight will be your Sun.

2. Move the flashlight and/or the globe so that the changes in the *length* of the shadow are the same as you observed for the sundial. Do not worry about whether the direction of the shadows is also accurate.

3. Record a description of how the length of the shadows changed. Then record a description of what you did to the globe and the flashlight to simulate the pattern of shadow lengths on a sundial. Write several sentences and sketch what you did.

Investigation 3: Make a Model to Show Changes in Both the Shadow's Length and Direction

Procedure

1. Use the same setup. The pencil should be attached to the globe at your location on Earth. It should point straight up from the center of the globe. The flashlight will be your Sun.

2. This time, move the flashlight and/or globe so that the changes in both the direction and length of the shadows are the same as they were on the sundial.

3. Record a description of the way the direction and length of the shadows changed. Then record a description of what you did to the globe and/or the flashlight to simulate the pattern of shadows on a sundial. Write several sentences and sketch what you did.

Reflect

1. Which motion or motions did you use to replicate the shadow pattern: spinning the globe, moving the flashlight, or both?

2. Answer this question if your answer to the first question was "both." Do you think spinning the globe and moving the flashlight are both necessary to replicate the shadow pattern? Why or why not?

3. Answer this question if your answer to the first question was only spinning the globe or only moving the flashlight but not both. Do you think you could produce the same pattern in the shadows by switching which object moves? Why or why not?

4. With your group, develop a claim about which movements of Earth and/or the Sun cause you to see the Sun move across the sky every day.

The Rotating Earth

In your model of the Sun and Earth, you used a globe mounted on an axis to represent Earth. Earth spins on an imaginary axis that extends through the North Pole and the South Pole. Earth spins in a counterclockwise direction as seen from above the North Pole. This is why the Sun appears to move across the sky from east to west.

The light side of Earth faces the Sun; it is daytime in every location on that side. The light from the Sun is blocked from the dark side; it is nighttime everywhere on the dark side. Notice that blue arrows are pointing counterclockwise. That is the direction in which Earth spins.

The person in the two diagrams below is standing on the same spot on Earth twelve hours apart. In the picture on the left, Earth is positioned so that in the place where the figure is standing sunlight appears. That person sees the Sun rise in the east and sees the sky become brighter as the Sun rises higher in the sky.

While that person experiences the Sun rise, people on the other side of Earth see the Sun set. Twelve hours later, Earth has rotated so that the place where the person is standing has moved from where the Sun is lighting up the region to a position where the Sun's light is blocked. The person, now in the picture on the right, sees the Sun disappear below the horizon and the outside becomes dark.

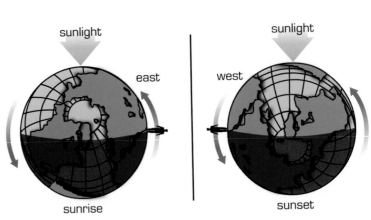

A person is standing at one point on Earth at sunrise (on left), and 12 hours later, the same person is standing at the same point on Earth at sunset (on right). Not to scale.

Imagine that you are the figure on the right. It is sunrise, and you see the Sun rising in the east. If you stood in that position until sunset, what would you see? It would appear to you that the Sun is moving across the sky from east to west. When the Sun sets, you will not be able to see it anymore. After sunset, the Sun's light is blocked by the light side of Earth.

day: the amount of time it takes a body to spin once on its axis.

Each day, you can watch the Sun rise (if it isn't cloudy or raining). After many hours of light, the Sun sets. After many hours of darkness, the Sun comes up again. During this time, from sunrise to sunrise, Earth completes one rotation on its axis. It takes about 24 hours for Earth to complete one rotation. The time it takes for one rotation is called a **day**.

Sunsets can produce spectacular displays of color.

Stop and Think

Revise your claim about which movements of Earth and/or the Sun cause us to see the Sun move across the sky every day. You can probably make your claim more complete and accurate now.

Explain

You probably understand more now about the movement of Earth and why you see the Sun move across the sky from east to west every day. You have already made a claim about the movement of Earth and/or the Sun. With your group, you will now develop an explanation statement of which movements of Earth and/or the Sun cause you to see the Sun move across the sky every day. Use a *Create an Explanation* page to help you develop your explanation statement. Remember that a good explanation has four features:

- your claim

- your evidence

- your science knowledge

- a statement connecting your claim to your evidence and the science you know

---

Create Your Explanation   1.BBQ.2/2.2.2/2.BBQ.3

Name:_____ Date:_____

Use this page to explain the lesson of your recent investigations.

Write a brief summary of the results from your investigation. You will use this summary to help you write your explanation.

Claim—a statement of what you understand or a conclusion that you have reached from an investigation or a set of investigations.

Evidence—data collected during investigations and trends in that data.

Science knowledge—knowledge about how things work. You may have learned this through reading, talking to an expert, discussion, or other experiences.

Write your explanation using your **Claim**, **Evidence** and **Science knowledge** from above.

© It's About Time

Begin by examining your claim. Your claim should be about which movements of Earth and/or the Sun cause you to see the Sun move across the sky every day. Make sure you still think your claim is correct. You may now wish to make your claim more complete or revise it. Record it in the appropriate box of your *Create Your Explanation* page.

Then work on supporting your claim with evidence and science knowledge. Your evidence can come from your examination of the sundial shadows, your model, or the diagrams you have been examining. Your evidence should support your claim about the way the Sun and/or Earth are moving. Then add science knowledge that supports your claim. Use what you learned from the reading.

After you have recorded your claim, evidence, and science knowledge, work on your explanation statement. It should use the evidence and science knowledge to support your claim. It should also be written in a way that helps someone reading it know the reasons why your claim is so. It should discuss the way movements of Earth and/or the Sun cause the apparent movement of the Sun across the sky and why we see the Sun moving when actually it is Earth that is moving. Make sure all the different parts of your explanation match each other.

Communicate

Share Your Explanation

Your class will now meet to share and discuss each group explanation. Working together, the class will then select and develop an explanation that best explains how Earth moves in relation to the Sun. This explanation will be supported by evidence from your investigations and other knowledge that you and your classmates can contribute.

Different people in the class may have different explanations. The class should decide together on one explanation. Alternate explanations should be recognized, and reasons why that explanation was not chosen should be given. The explanation you choose can include questions that need to be answered. You may also have ideas for other tests that can be performed to prove whether this explanation is right or wrong.

Update the *Project Board*

Now that you have completed an explanation about the apparent motion of the Sun based on your observations and models, it is a good time to update the *Project Board*. You will focus on the two columns *What are we learning?* and *What is our evidence?* When you record what you are learning in the third column, you may be confirming some of the things you think you know from the first column. Or, you may be answering some of the questions you recorded in the *What do we need to investigate?* column.

What's the Point?

Because Earth is spinning, each day the Sun first appears, or rises, in the east. The Sun then seems to travel west, rising higher in the sky and reaching its highest point at midday. After midday, the Sun appears to continue traveling west and to get lower in the sky, until it disappears, or sets, in the west. However, it is not the Sun that is moving. Instead, it is Earth's rotation that makes the Sun appear to move across the sky.

2.3 Explore

Where Is the Moon Located, and How Does It Move?

The different shapes of the Moon are familiar sights in the night sky, but not everyone knows why the Moon appears to move across the sky and to change shape during each month.

The second brightest object in Earth's sky, much closer to Earth than the Sun, is the Moon. The Moon is probably the most observed object in our solar system. Most people can tell you features of the Moon or, perhaps, some old stories about what makes up the Moon. However, not everyone knows how the Moon moves across the sky and why it changes its appearance the way it does. In this section you will investigate the Moon's apparent motion across the sky and work to figure out its location in relation to Earth and the way it actually moves.

Investigation 1: The Moon's Path in One Day

You will investigate the Moon's apparent motion across the sky in a single day and then compare this motion to the apparent motion of the Sun. You saw that the Sun's apparent movement across the sky is caused by Earth's motion. As you explore the Moon's location and movement, keep that in mind. Perhaps the Moon's movement is also related to Earth's motion.

Procedure

1. With your group, examine Image #1, which shows the Moon's position every two hours as seen from Earth on a day in June.

2. Then examine Image #2, which shows the Sun's position every two hours as seen on the same day from the same location on Earth.

Image 1

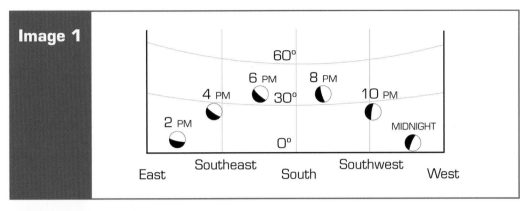

Image 2

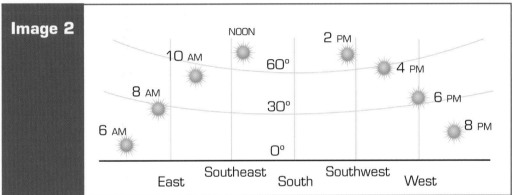

3. With your group, compare the apparent motion of the Moon to that of the Sun. Using a chart like the one below, identify the ways that the motions are similar and the ways they are different.

Comparing the Apparent Motions of the Moon and Sun	
Similarities	**Differences**

East   South   West

June 25   8:30 PM

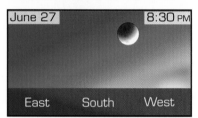

East   South   West

June 27   8:30 PM

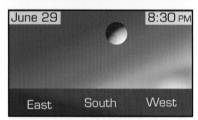

East   South   West

June 29   8:30 PM

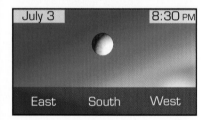

East   South   West

July 3   8:30 PM

East   South   West

July 7   8:30 PM

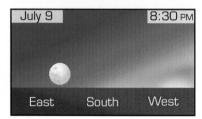

East   South   West

July 9   8:30 PM

The Moon at sunset over 2 weeks. Not to scale.

Analyze Your Data

1. Compare the path the Moon appears to take across the sky to the path the Sun appears to take. How are the paths similar? How are they different?

2. How would you describe to a friend where to find the Moon on this day if your friend first finds the Sun?

3. Where is the Moon when the Sun sets?

4. As seen from the continental United States, the Sun rises once each day and sets once each day. What can you conclude about how often the Moon rises and sets?

Reflect

1. A classmate states that the Moon cannot be seen during the daytime. Do you agree or disagree? Provide supporting evidence from your observations of the images.

2. A classmate concludes that the Moon's path across the sky is always lower than the Sun's path across the sky. What observations could you make to test whether this is true?

3. Think back to the last time you saw a full moon. How is the appearance of a full moon different from the appearance of the Moon in the image?

4. What else do you think you need to know about the Moon's changing appearance to describe its apparent motion?

Investigation 2: The Moon's Position and Appearance Over Two Weeks

You know something now about the way the Moon moves over the course of a day. But you also know that the Moon's appearance in the sky changes from week to week—even from night to night. In this investigation, you will examine how the position of the Moon changes over a two-week period. Then you will use those changes to imagine how the Moon moves.

Procedure

1. With your group, look at the sequences of images of the Moon on the previous page. These images show the position of the Moon at sunset every two or four days for a period of two weeks.

2. Discuss the changes in the Moon's position and appearance with your group. Record your observations in a chart like the one below.

The Moon's Appearance Over Two Weeks			
Date and time	How high is the Moon?	Direction to look for the Moon	Apparent shape of the Moon

Analyze Your Data

1. Describe the changes in the apparent shape of the Moon during the two weeks.

2. When does the Moon appear to be closest to the Sun at sunset? When does the Moon appear to be farthest from the Sun at sunset?

3. When does the Moon appear lowest in the sky at sunset? When does the Moon appear highest at sunset?

4. Suppose you and a friend together observe the Moon at sunset tonight. How would you describe to your friend where to find the Moon tomorrow night at sunset?

Reflect

1. How is the changing position of the Moon over two weeks similar to the changes you observed in the images you used, for the investigation (the Moon's motion during one day)? How is the changing position of the Moon over two weeks different from the changes that occur in one day?

2. In which direction is the Moon's position at sunset shifting, east to west or west to east? What do you think is the reason for the shift being in this direction?

PBIS

reflection:
bouncing back
of light from a
surface.

reflected:
bounced back off a
surface.

Moonlight

When you look in a mirror, you are looking at your **reflection**. Light bounces off you, travels to the mirror, and bounces off the mirror. This **reflected** light enters your eye, and your brain interprets the light as an image. The mirror does not make light; it only reflects the light that strikes it from another source. A good mirror reflects about 95 percent of the light that hits it.

Solar-system objects also reflect light. The source of the light they reflect is the Sun. The Sun, the only star in our solar system, is the only solar-system object that produces its own light. All other objects in the solar system reflect the Sun's light, including Earth. This reflected light is what enables you to see these objects.

Some solar-system objects reflect more light than others. The Moon's soil is light gray and made up of broken rocks and dust. Some of the rocks and dust come from collisions with other solar-system objects. When sunlight strikes the Moon, some is absorbed and some is reflected. The gray, uneven surface of the Moon only reflects about 7 percent of the sunlight. This is much less than the light reflected by a good mirror, yet it is enough to make the Moon appear to shine brightly in the sky.

If you stood on the Moon and looked at Earth, you would see Earth shining in the night sky the same way you see the Moon from Earth. However, Earth would shine more brightly. Earth's surface is about three times more reflective than the Moon's. Enceladus, one of the planet Saturn's moons, is covered entirely in ice. This smooth, shiny surface reflects 99 percent of the sunlight that strikes it, making it the brightest moon in our solar system.

Taken by Apollo 8 astronaut Bill Anders in 1968, this is a photograph of Earth rising beyond the Moon's horizon. Earth is shining with reflected sunlight.

AST 84

Reflect

1. On the previous page is a photograph of Earth and the Moon taken from space. Only part of Earth is illuminated. How could reflected sunlight on Earth account for Earth not looking like a sphere in the photograph?

2. Where do you think the Sun is located in this picture—to the left, to the right, above, or below Earth and the Moon? How do you know?

Phases of the Moon

Observing the Moon over several months, you would see the same pattern of different lunar shapes repeated month after month, just as ancient astronomers observed thousands of years ago. Looking closely, you can see that what is changing is actually the portion of the Moon that is illuminated. The different illuminated portions of the Moon as seen from Earth are called the **phases of the Moon**.

The phases of the Moon are part of a cycle that takes a little less than a month to complete. The cycle begins with none of the Moon visible. This phase is called the *new moon.* During the next two weeks, you can observe a little more of the Moon being illuminated each day. These are the phases you investigated in the six images of the Moon at sunset.

phase of the Moon: the illuminated part of the Moon visible from Earth at a given time.

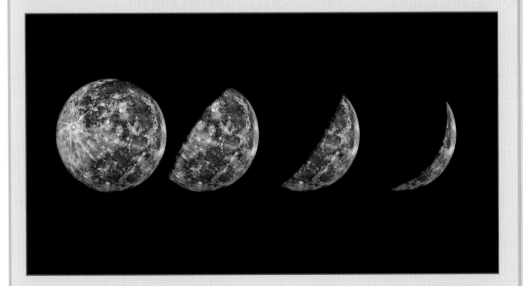

One week after new moon, the right half of the Moon is illuminated. This phase is called the *first quarter moon*. After two weeks, the visible Moon looks like a complete circle. It is called a *full moon*. During the two weeks after the full moon, you can observe that less and less of the Moon is illuminated each day. One week after the full moon, the left half of the Moon is illuminated. This phase is called the *last quarter moon*. The cycle begins again two weeks after the full moon, when once more none of the Moon is visible and the Moon is back in the new moon phase.

Stop and Think

1. How much of the Moon is illuminated at any particular time?

2. At the first quarter moon, how much of the illuminated part of the Moon can you see?

3. At the full moon, how much of the illuminated part of the Moon can you see?

4. Why do you think that you see more of the illuminated part of the Moon at full moon than at the first quarter moon?

Make a Model of the Motions of the Earth-Moon-Sun System

Knowing that the Moon reflects light from the Sun, and does not produce its own light, provides a clue as to why the Moon changes in appearance. However, you may not yet understand enough about the interactions among Earth, the Sun, and the Moon to be able to fully explain the Moon's changes in appearance. To help you develop that understanding, you will explore how motions of Earth, the Sun, and the Moon result in the changing appearance of the Moon as seen from Earth.

Before you start the activity, think back to the model you made of the Sun and Earth. You used a flashlight to represent the Sun. You used your Sun to make shadows of a pencil on a globe representing Earth. In that model, two types of motion were possible: Earth could spin on its axis or the flashlight (the Sun) could move around Earth. You found that the rotation, or spin, of Earth could explain why the Sun appears to move across the sky.

This time you will be observing a different type of movement—the movement of one solar-system object around another one. The path that one solar-system object takes in moving around another object is called an **orbit**. You may also say that one object orbits the other object.

For this next model, three objects are involved, one each to represent Earth, the Sun, and the Moon. Your task is to determine what combination of objects rotating and objects orbiting one another accounts for changes in the Moon's phases and our view of the phases. You will start by looking only at the Moon's motion and then add in Earth's motion.

orbit: the path that a solar-system object takes in revolving around another solar-system object.

Investigation 3: Simulate the Motion of the Moon

Procedure

Materials
- **styrene ball to represent the Moon**
- **wooden splint**
- **flashlight**

1. Mount the styrene ball on the wooden splint. The ball will represent the Moon. Do not push the wooden splint all the way through the styrene ball.

2. You will set up a light source to represent the Sun. In this demonstration, the Sun will not move.

3. In this model, your head will represent Earth. Your eyes are like the eyes of an observer on Earth's surface.

4. Each group member will have a chance to hold the model Moon and observe the phase of the model Moon. When it is your turn, stand with your back to the model Sun. Hold the model Moon in front of you at arm's length, a little higher than your head. Holding it like this will allow observers standing behind you to see. You should be able to see that one half of the ball is illuminated. The entire illuminated half is facing you.

5. While the first group member holds the model Moon, discuss as a group which phase of the Moon you are observing. After you reach agreement, sketch the phase in the correct row of the table on your *Phases of the Moon* page.

6. While each group member holds the model Moon, the others should record the positions of Earth, the Sun, and the Moon in the correct row of their *Phases of the Moon* pages. You are not making a scale drawing; this is just a diagram to show the angle between the Sun, Earth, and the Moon. Your diagram should be a top-down view, as if you were observing from the ceiling. The position of the Sun has already been recorded for you in each diagram. To record the positions of Earth and the Moon, you will write an *E* in one circle and an *M* in one circle.

7. Discuss as a group any differences in your sketches or diagrams, and come to an agreement about which sketch or diagram you think is best.

8. Repeat Steps 5–7, but this time, as you hold the Moon, rotate left one-quarter circle so that your left side is facing the model Sun. Again, hold the model Moon in front of you at arm's length, slightly higher than your head. One half of the model Moon is still illuminated by the model Sun, but your view of the illuminated half has changed.

9. Repeat Steps 5–7, but this time rotate left another one-quarter circle so that you are facing the model Sun.

10. Repeat Steps 5–7, but this time rotate left another one-quarter of a circle so that your right side is facing the model Sun.

horizon: the line at which the sky and Earth appear to meet.

lunar horizon: the line at which the sky and Moon appear to meet.

In this photo taken from NASA's Clementine spacecraft, the Moon (right corner) is illuminated solely by light reflected from Earth. The bright glow on the lunar horizon is from the edge of the Sun. The bright spot on the top is the planet Venus.

Investigation 4: Simulate the Motions of the Moon and Earth

You will now try to simulate how the Moon and Earth move at the same time.

Procedure

1. Start by modeling Planet X and its moon. Planet X, like Earth, rotates on its axis once per day. The moon of Planet X also takes one day to make one complete orbit. To model this, hold the model moon in front of you at arm's length, slightly above the top of your head. Rotate slowly in place. Record your observations of the phases of the moon. Describe how one complete rotation of the planet compares with one complete orbit of the moon.

2. Let each group member take a turn repeating Step 1. Watch as each group member simulates Planet X's motion.

3. Now you will simulate Planet Y and its moon. Planet Y, like Earth, rotates on its axis once per day. However, the moon of Planet Y takes four days to orbit Planet Y. This simulation will require two group members. One member of your group will be Planet Y. Another will hold the plastic foam ball to represent Planet Y's moon. Planet Y should spin once in 10 seconds, and the model moon should take 40 seconds to complete an orbit. Practice this, and decide as a group that you are simulating the movement of Planet Y and its moon correctly. When you are satisfied that you are simulating the motion of the spinning planet and orbiting moon correctly, the student representing Planet Y should observe the moon's phases and record observations of the phases.

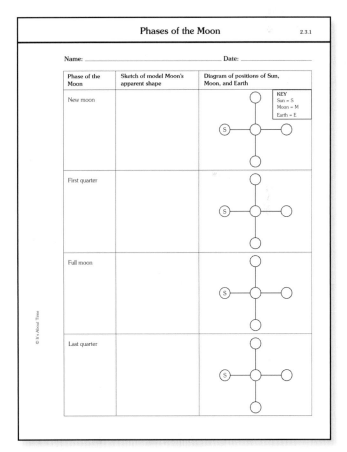

ASTRONOMY

4. Let each group member take a turn as Planet Y. Those who are not in the simulation should watch carefully.

5. Now you are ready to model Earth and the Moon. Remember that it takes about one week, or seven days, to go from new moon to the first quarter moon. You will need to determine how long it takes for the Moon to move through all of its phases. Decide on that as a group, then practice simulating the motion of Earth and the Moon. Agree as a group that you are simulating the motion correctly. When you are satisfied that you are simulating the motion of the spinning Earth and the orbiting Moon correctly, the person representing Earth should observe the Moon's phases and record observations of the phases. When you record these, you should be describing how an observer on Earth sees the phase of the Moon during one day.

6. Let each group member take a turn as Earth. Those who are not in the simulation should watch carefully.

Communicate

Share Your Ideas

When all the groups have completed their investigations, you will work as a class to make sense of the data you have collected.

One group member will simulate Planet X and its moon. During the presentation, another group member will describe what is happening.

As you watch and listen, notice what was the same as and what was different from the simulation your group did. If your group did something different, raise your hand and ask for permission to show your group's simulation to the class. Then, as a class, decide which simulation is most accurate and why. Or combine the best of each simulation to develop a more accurate simulation than any of the groups has presented. Then answer these questions.

1. In what order do the phases occur?

2. In what direction does the moon orbit the planet as seen from above?

3. About what fraction of its orbit does the moon move during the time it takes the planet to spin once on its axis?

If you have trouble answering any of these questions, ask questions to the class. If you disagree with the answers, respectfully offer your thoughts and ideas for improvement.

Repeat this sequence for Planet Y and its moon, and for Earth and the Moon.

Reflect

1. Remember that the shape of the Moon is a sphere. At the full moon, how much of the Moon's surface is illuminated? How much of the Moon's surface is illuminated at the new moon?

2. Imagine that a person in Florida and a person in California observe the Moon on the same night. Do both people see the same phase of the Moon? Why or why not?

3. Simply by looking at the Sun and the Moon in the sky, there is no way to tell how far apart they are. However, you had to make some assumptions about how far apart the three objects were. What assumptions did you use in your model?

4. If the Sun orbited Earth to cause day and night, what problems might this pose for your model of the phases of the Moon?

Motions of the Earth-Moon-Sun System and Phases of the Moon

As you may have noticed, the Moon's changes in appearance can be explained by the Moon's orbit around Earth. The Moon is visible because sunlight is reflected from its surface. Half of the Moon is always illuminated, but only at the full moon is the entire illuminated portion of the Moon facing Earth.

Phases of the Moon depend on how Earth, the Moon, and the Sun are positioned relative to one another. As the Moon orbits Earth, the angles among the Sun, Earth, and the Moon change. At the new moon, the Moon is located between Earth and the Sun, and the side of the Moon that is illuminated faces away from Earth. You do not see the Moon because the side you are looking at is dark. At the full moon, the Moon is on the side of Earth opposite the Sun. The illuminated side of the Moon is facing toward Earth, so the entire illuminated side of the Moon is visible.

Just as Earth spins on its axis, the Moon also spins on an axis. Since the Moon takes the same amount of time to rotate once on its axis as it does to revolve once around Earth, the same side of the Moon always faces Earth. This is why the pattern of the craters you see on the Moon's surface is always the same. We only see one side of the Moon from Earth. Only by taking pictures from space or by traveling to the Moon is it possible to see the Moon's other side (the far side of the Moon).

It takes about 29.5 days to complete one cycle of the Moon's phases; for example, from new moon to new moon. This is a little longer than the time it takes the Moon to orbit Earth because Earth and the Sun have shifted positions relative to each other during that time. Just as a day on Earth is based on the natural cycle of daylight and darkness, a month is approximately based on the natural cycles of the phases of the Moon.

When the illuminated part of the Moon appears to grow smaller, the Moon is waning. When the illuminated part appears to grow larger, the Moon is waxing.

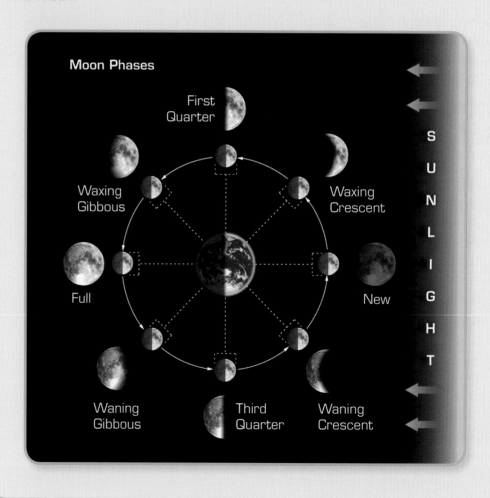

Moon Phases

First Quarter

Waxing Gibbous

Waxing Crescent

Full

New

Waning Gibbous

Third Quarter

Waning Crescent

S U N L I G H T

Revise Your Explanation

Earlier you wrote a claim and explanation statement about the apparent motion of the Sun in the sky. First, you will revise that explanation to include new information so that the apparent motion of the Sun is accounted for on your *Create Your Explanation* page. Next, you will develop a second statement that explains the apparent motion of the Moon during one month. Your claim will be the Moon's apparent motion and your explanation statement will include why people see it that way. This explanation should also account for the changing phases of the Moon. Record your explanation on another *Create Your Explanation* page.

Communicate

Share Your Explanation

Your class will now meet to share and discuss your explanations. Working together, the class will select and develop an explanation that best explains the apparent motion of the Sun and of the Moon. This explanation will be supported by evidence from your investigations and other knowledge that you and your classmates can contribute.

Reflect

1. How would you go about trying to prove that Earth is closer to the Moon than to the Sun?

2. Suppose a new space object is found: Asteroid Q2010. Astronomers study it for weeks and see that it is moving slowly in a straight line. The motions of Earth, the Moon, and the Sun are predictable. What does this indicate to you about the likelihood of determining whether Asteroid Q2010 will collide with Earth, the Moon, or the Sun?

3. Now suppose that another asteroid is identified, Asteroid Z2010, but astronomers do not yet know which way it is moving. What does this tell you about the likelihood of determining whether Asteroid Q2010 will collide with Asteroid Z2010?

Update the *Project Board*

Now that you have explained the apparent motion of both the Sun and the Moon, it is a good time to update the *Project Board*. Add what you know about Earth's rotation, the Moon's apparent motion, and the Moon's phases to the *What are we learning?* column. Make sure to add evidence to the *What is our evidence?* column. In the *What do we think we know?* column, include anything you think affects the likelihood of objects colliding. If you still have questions about the location and motion of objects in the solar system, record them in the *What do we need to investigate?* column.

How can you know if objects in space will collide?				
What do we think we know?	What do we need to investigate?	What are we learning?	What is our evidence?	What does it mean for the challenge or question?

What's the Point?

The rotation of Earth causes the daily apparent motion of the Moon across the sky. Earth spins on its axis once per day. This is why the Moon, like the Sun, rises once each day and sets once each day. Like the Sun, the Moon rises in the east, moves across the sky, and then sets in the west.

The phases of the Moon are determined by the angle between Earth, the Sun, and the Moon. As the Moon moves in its path around Earth, one-half of the Moon (the side facing the Sun) is always illuminated. Because different amounts of the illuminated side face Earth, the Moon appears in different phases.

2.4 Explore

How Do the Sizes of Earth and the Moon Compare, and How Far Apart Are They?

When you are going on a trip, you may be watching for a famous landmark; for example, a statue or a lighthouse. When you spot the landmark in the distance, it may look tiny. As you get closer to your destination, the structure appears to get larger and larger. You don't realize its great size until you are finally right next to it, and then you might realize how small you are compared to it.

To determine whether objects are likely to collide with Earth, the Moon, or the Sun, it is important to know how big they are. Both the Sun and the Moon appear to be about the same size in the sky. Does that mean they *are* the same size? Just from looking at the sky, there is no way to determine their actual size or how far apart they are. But if you can determine the distance to each object, then you can tell how large each object must be for it to appear the way it does in the sky.

This photograph of Earth and the Moon was taken from Mars, which is 192 million km (115 million mi) away. The brightness of the Moon has been enhanced to make it more visible.

Predict

A globe is often used to represent Earth. If this were the size of Earth, how big do you think the Moon would be, using the same scale? Maybe you think the Moon would be the size of a softball, about one quarter the size of Earth. Or, maybe you think the Moon is more like a marble, about one hundredth the size of Earth. Or, perhaps you think the right size is somewhere in between.

Decide what spherical object you think would be most like the size of the Moon. Share your ideas with your group and discuss what knowledge you used to choose your object. You may change the object you have chosen based on your discussion.

Once your group has settled on an object that would represent the Moon, use available resources to determine the diameter of the object you have chosen. Then measure the diameter of the globe you have used in the previous activities. After that, divide the diameter of the globe by the diameter of the sphere that represents the Moon. This will give you a prediction of the relative sizes of Earth and the Moon.

Build a Scale Model of Earth and the Moon

You will now build and analyze a scale model of the Earth-Moon system. You will use clay to model Earth and the Moon. As you work through the procedure, keep in mind your prediction about the sizes of these two solar-system bodies. Think about how accurately you predicted the relative size of each object.

Materials

- clay
- toothpicks
- ruler
- meter stick

Procedure

1. Break the clay into 50 equal parts. Roll them into balls using your hands so that you can easily compare their sizes. Do not worry if some are slightly bigger than others; the pieces do not have to be exactly the same size.

2. Take one of the 50 little balls and set it aside. Use the other 49 pieces and combine them to create a larger ball. The smaller ball, which is $\frac{1}{50}$ of the original amount of clay, represents the size of the Moon. The larger ball, which is $\frac{49}{50}$ of the original amount of clay, represents the size of Earth.

3. Use your ruler to measure the diameter of each ball. Record your measurements, then find the ratio of the diameter of Earth to the diameter of the Moon by dividing the two numbers.

Reflect

1. Compare the ratio from your clay model to the ratio you calculated in your prediction. How did the results of this activity compare to the prediction you made about the relative size of the Moon compared to Earth?

2. Most people think the Moon is much larger than it actually is, compared to Earth. What surprised you about the relative size of the Moon compared to Earth?

3. The diameter of the Sun is about 110 times the diameter of Earth. How big would the Sun be in your model, if it were made to the same scale?

Predict

You have created two scale objects showing that the volume of Earth is 49 times greater than the volume of the Moon. Now you will complete your model by determining how far apart your Earth model and Moon model should be.

Start by predicting how far apart the model Earth and model Moon should be in your scale model. Select one set of clay balls made by a member of your group. Work with your group to come to an agreement on how far apart Earth and the Moon should be. Measure and record that distance. Discuss with your group if you think that distance is too small or too large. Adjust the distance if you wish, repeating the measurement if necessary. Be prepared to share your prediction, and the reasons for it, with the class.

Communicate

Share Your Ideas

When each group has finished making their predictions, share them with the class. As each group shares their prediction, make a record of it along with a note about the reasons for their prediction. You may want to make a poster for the classroom with all of the predictions on it. This way you can compare and discuss each group's ideas.

Model the Distance Between Earth and the Moon

You have predicted the distance between Earth and the Moon. Now you will use the model to find the actual scale distance.

Procedure

1. Measure the diameter of your Earth model using a toothpick. Push the toothpick through the clay model of Earth. Try to push the toothpick in so that it passes through the middle of the sphere and a little bit of it is coming out of both sides. Mark the toothpick on each side of the sphere where it touches the sphere.

2. Remove the toothpick and measure between the two marks. This will tell you the diameter of your Earth. Record this measurement to the nearest tenth of a centimeter.

3. To find the actual distance between Earth and the Moon, multiply this distance by 30. Use a meter stick to measure the correct distance from your clay Earth. Place your Moon model at the correct distance from your Earth model.

Reflect

1. How did the correct distance from Earth to the Moon in the scale model compare to the distance you predicted? List reasons why the evidence you used helped your prediction be accurate or led to your prediction being inaccurate.

2. Think about how large the Moon appears in the sky. How does the model help you explain why the Moon is the size that it is?

3. The diameter of the Sun is about 400 times the diameter of the Moon. Yet the Sun and the Moon appear to be about the same size in the sky. How much farther away do you think the Sun must be from Earth than the Moon? Give evidence to support your answer.

4. Use your answer from Question 3 to determine how far away from Earth you would place the Sun in your scale model.

The Celestial Sphere

Astronomers sometimes describe what we observe in the sky as the *celestial sphere.* The celestial sphere is an imaginary sphere surrounding Earth, upon which all the objects observed in the sky are drawn. It does not account for the different distances the objects are from Earth, but it does help you understand what objects are observed from your location on Earth and their relative motions. A person looking at the night sky can see at most half of the celestial sphere.

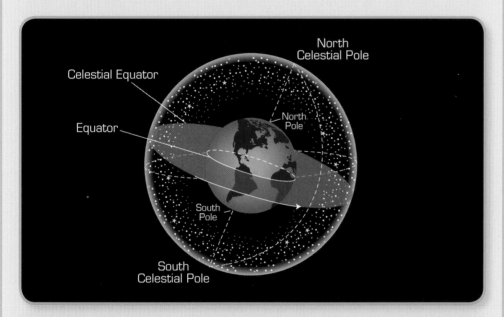

degree: a unit of measure for angles. A complete circle is 360°. (360 degrees)

The scientific definition of a day is one rotation of Earth. But people also use day and night to distinguish between the time when the Sun is visible and the time when it is not. During the night, stars and planets are visible unless clouds, dust, and light from cities and towns obscure the view. During the day, Earth's atmosphere scatters sunlight across the whole sky. The sky is so bright that it washes out the rest of the celestial sphere so that only the Sun, the Moon, and occasionally Venus, are bright enough to be visible during the day. The Moon is not always visible during the day. The Moon is only visible when it is above the horizon and not in the new moon phase.

The Sun is the only star close enough to Earth to look like a sphere. The other stars are so far away that they are seen as very bright, tiny points of light, even when viewed through a telescope. The atmosphere scatters the starlight, causing it to appear to be coming from slightly different points in the sky from moment to moment. The result is that the stars twinkle. You can tell if you are looking at a planet in the sky because planets don't twinkle. The planets are close enough to appear as tiny spheres through binoculars or a telescope, so the light does not "jump around" as you look at them.

If you could view stars from the Moon they would not twinkle because the Moon has no atmosphere. Astronauts have reported that, in space, stars appear as brilliant points of light. You also could see more easily that different stars have different colors if you viewed them from the Moon or from space.

When you think of the sky as a celestial sphere, you can think of the twinkling stars as a fixed background. Stars may rise and set as you watch on a given night, but they stay nearly fixed relative to each other. That is why we see the same constellations of stars that people saw thousands of years ago. The shapes have hardly changed at all.

A convenient method for estimating sizes and distances on the celestial sphere is to use your hands to measure **degrees**. A degree is a unit of measure for angles. To understand what a degree is, imagine a circle. A complete circle is 360° (360 degrees). One degree (1°) is $\frac{1}{360}$ of a circle.

The width of your fist, held at arm's length, covers about 10° of the sky. Your thumb, also held at arm's length, covers about 2°, and your pinky finger covers about 1°. You can practice estimating with hand measurements by starting with something familiar. Hold your fist out in front of you at arm's length, pointing to the horizon. Place your other fist, also at arm's length, on top of your first fist. Alternate fists until you have gone nine fists up from the horizon, which would equal 90°. The last fist you make should be pointing straight up. This is because one quarter of a circle is equal to 90° (360° divided by 4).

Never look at the Sun. It is very dangerous to look directly at the Sun.

Try measuring a familiar object in the night sky, such as the Big Dipper. The Big Dipper should be a little more than twice the width of a fist held at arm's length, or 25°. Once you are comfortable with the technique, use it to estimate the width of the Moon and the Sun. Think about how the Moon's size might compare with the size of the Sun. At sunset, without looking directly at the Sun, you can safely estimate the width of the Sun by blocking its light.

The width of two of your fists side by side equals about 20°. The Big Dipper is about 25° across.

What's the Point?

The diameter of the Sun is about 110 times the diameter of Earth, and Earth is a little less than four times the diameter of the Moon. The distance between Earth and the Moon is about 30 times Earth's diameter. The distance from Earth to the Sun is about 400 times the distance from Earth to the Moon. From our perspective, Earth seems very large. However, it is very small compared to the size of the Sun. When you consider the distance from Earth to the Sun, you will realize how much larger the Sun is than it appears when observed from Earth.

The celestial sphere is the appearance of the sky from Earth. The stars can be considered points fixed relative to one another on the celestial sphere. Viewed against this background, the Sun and the Moon appear to be the same size, about one half a degree in diameter. Yet, the size of the Sun and the Moon are very different from each other, and they are very different distances from Earth.

With advanced space exploration technology on Earth and in satellites, astronomers can further their understanding of distant objects in space.

2.5 Explore

What Do Eclipses Tell You About Distances to the Sun and the Moon?

In the year 585 B.C.E., in what is now Iran, two armies had been at war with each other for five years. One day, as they were engaged in battle, suddenly "the day was turned into night." The armies saw it as a sign to stop fighting immediately. Although the Sun soon reappeared, a treaty was signed, and the war was over.

This event, reported by the Greek historian Herodotus, may very well have been an **eclipse**. Eclipse means to cut off or block a view. An eclipse occurs when an object in space partially or totally blocks the light by which we see another object in space. Two types of eclipses are **solar eclipses** and **lunar eclipses**. In a solar eclipse, the Moon blocks our view of the Sun. In a lunar eclipse, the Moon moves into Earth's shadow, so the Moon is no longer seen by reflected sunlight.

In the last section, you discovered that the Sun and the Moon appear to be about the same size in the sky. This is an interesting coincidence, because it means that both objects can have a **total eclipse**. A total eclipse happens when one space object totally blocks the light by which we see another object in space. Sometimes an eclipse is partial. In a **partial eclipse**, only part of a space object disappears from view.

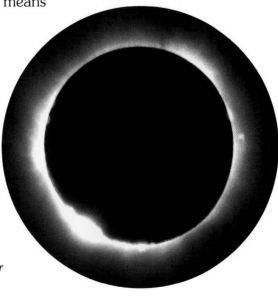

During a total solar eclipse, the Moon passes between the Sun and Earth, so Earth becomes dark. At any single location on Earth, total solar eclipses occur rarely, about once every 370 years.

eclipse: the blocking of light from one object in space by another object in space, as seen from a particular location.

solar eclipse: when the Moon passes between the Sun and Earth, so that light from the Sun is partially or totally blocked.

lunar eclipse: when the Moon passes through Earth's shadow so that some or all of the Moon can only be seen by reflected light from Earth.

total eclipse: the complete blocking of light from one object in space by another object in space, as seen from a particular location.

partial eclipse: the blocking of a portion of light from one object in space by another object in space, as seen from a particular location.

An eclipse of the Sun, or a solar eclipse, occurs when the Moon passes between the Sun and Earth, and our view of the Sun is partially or completely blocked. This can happen only when the Moon is directly between Earth and the Sun. At the new moon, the Moon is between Earth and the Sun, but an eclipse does not occur at every new moon. Often, the Moon's path takes it above or below the line connecting Earth and the Sun, in which case a partial eclipse or no eclipse occurs.

umbra: the dark, inner shadow cast by an object.

penumbra: the lighter, outer shadow cast by an object; the penumbra surrounds the umbra.

A shadow can have two parts. The **umbra** is the darker, inner shadow. The **penumbra** is the larger, outer shadow. During a solar eclipse, the Moon's penumbra can fall on Earth, and people in those areas on Earth experience a total eclipse. This is where the Moon blocks only part of the Sun's rays. Total solar eclipses occur somewhere on Earth an average of every 18 months. However, at any given location, total solar eclipses take place on average once every 370 years. Total solar eclipses are always shorter than 8 minutes at a given location on Earth.

An eclipse of the Moon, or lunar eclipse, occurs when the Moon passes through some part of Earth's shadow. Lunar eclipses are much more common, because Earth's umbra is larger than the Moon at the distance that the Moon orbits Earth. Total lunar eclipses occur on average more than once a year, and can last as long as two hours.

Partial solar eclipse.

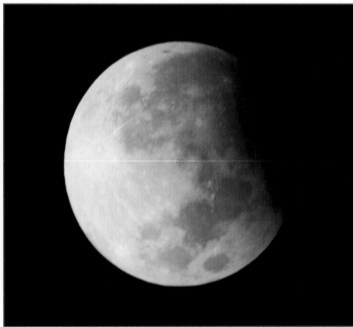

Partial lunar eclipse.

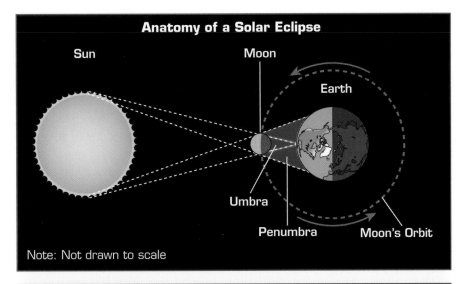

Anatomy of a Solar Eclipse

Sun

Moon

Earth

Umbra

Penumbra

Moon's Orbit

Note: Not drawn to scale

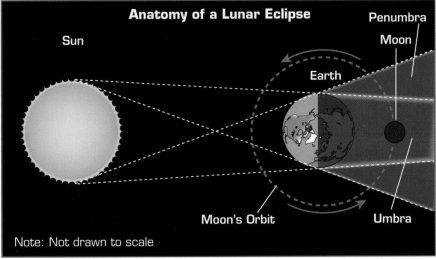

Anatomy of a Lunar Eclipse

Penumbra

Sun

Moon

Earth

Moon's Orbit

Umbra

Note: Not drawn to scale

Materials

- bright light source
- globe
- styrene ball
- wooden splint

Model a Solar Eclipse

Working with your group, use the same setup you used when modeling the phases of the Moon to demonstrate a solar eclipse. Use a flashlight for the Sun, a ball for the Moon, and a globe for Earth. When you have successfully aligned your objects so the Moon is blocking the light of the Sun from reaching part of the globe, sketch the alignment. Make sure that in your sketch you label all the different parts of the shadow cast by the Moon that you see.

Stop and Think

Use your sketch to answer the following questions:

1. How much of Earth do you think can be covered by the shadow of the Moon? Why do you think this?

2. During what phase of the Moon can a solar eclipse occur? How much of the Moon is visible during a solar eclipse?

fusion reaction: a change in which one or more low-mass elements produces a higher-mass element, with a release of enormous amounts of energy.

corona: outer portion of the Sun's atmosphere, consisting of superheated gases.

The Sun

Like all stars, the Sun is a hot ball composed mostly of hydrogen and helium. Its temperature is about 5700°C at its surface. This seems pretty hot, until you learn that at the center of the Sun, the temperature is nearly 14,000,000°C! This is hot enough to smash together two hydrogen atoms to form a helium atom. This is called a **fusion reaction**, and it releases the energy that life on Earth needs to survive.

The Sun also has an atmosphere, part of which is called the **corona**. The corona is composed of superheated gases. Normally, the surface of the Sun is so bright that the dimmer corona usually cannot be seen from Earth. But during a total solar eclipse, the corona is visible as a band of hot gas that surrounds the darkened disk of the Sun.

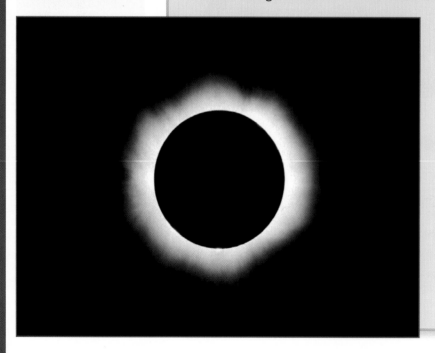

Looking at the Sun, even through most filters, can severely damage your eyes and even cause blindness. Scientists use other means to observe the Sun's disk, such as using special filters and mirrors to observe a projection of the Sun on a screen. If you observe such an image over a period of time, you will discover that the Sun's appearance changes from day to day. Like the Moon, the Sun's appearance can change, but the Sun's changes are more difficult to observe.

The Sun's image contains dark spots called sunspots. These spots are still very bright; they look dark only in comparison to the rest of the Sun. Sunspots rotate around the Sun, which shows that the Sun also rotates on an axis, much like Earth and the Moon.

An active sunspot viewed sideways.

Model a Lunar Eclipse

Work with your group, and use the setup from the phases of the Moon activity to model a lunar eclipse. When you have successfully aligned the Sun, Earth, and the Moon to form a total lunar eclipse, make a drawing. Make sure you label the umbra and penumbra in your drawing.

Stop and Think

Use your drawing to answer the following questions:

1. During what phase of the Moon can a lunar eclipse occur? What part of the Moon, if any, can be seen during a lunar eclipse?

2. Can a lunar eclipse occur at night? Why or why not?

3. From where on Earth might a lunar eclipse be visible?

Reflect

1. What would someone on the Moon see when facing Earth during a total solar eclipse on Earth? Why?

2. What would happen to the number and length of lunar and solar eclipses if the Moon were twice the diameter that it actually is?

3. Some people have trouble remembering the correct term for the two types of eclipses. What is a good way to remember the difference that you can teach to a friend?

4. Why do people rarely see a total solar eclipse, while many people have seen a total lunar eclipse?

What's the Point?

During the new moon, a solar eclipse may occur. If the Moon passes directly between the Sun and Earth, the shadow of the Moon falls on Earth and our view of the Sun is partially or completely blocked. A lunar eclipse may occur only at the full moon. Earth's shadow falls on the Moon.

Just a narrow sliver of the full moon is visible during this lunar eclipse.

More to Learn

How Are Tides Caused by Gravity of the Sun and the Moon?

Earth and the other planets are kept in orbit around the Sun by the Sun's gravity. Any two objects pull on each other because of the force of gravity. The more massive an object is, the greater the force of gravity pulls on another object. The Sun is much more massive than Earth, so Earth is prevented from moving off into space and is instead pulled into orbit around the Sun. In the same way, the Moon is pulled into orbit around Earth because Earth is much more massive than the Moon.

However, the Moon's gravity does have an effect on Earth. If you live near the ocean, or if you have visited the seashore, you know that the line where the water reaches the shore changes dramatically throughout the day. **Tides** are the rise and fall of water in the oceans. There can be two high tides and two low tides in a 24-hour period, with the highest and lowest levels occurring about every 6 hours.

Tides are caused by the gravitational attraction between Earth and the Moon. The Moon's gravity distorts the sea level so that the sea is slightly higher on the side of Earth closer to the Moon and also on the side farther from the Moon. As Earth spins on its axis, the part of Earth that faces the Moon changes. When a location is oriented so that it faces toward the Moon, or opposite the Moon, the bulge of water is at its highest point, and there is a **high tide**. Between the two bulges are low areas, because water has been pulled away to form the bulge. A location in one of these low areas has a **low tide**.

At any given location on Earth, several factors affect when tides occur, including the local landscape and water depth. However, the biggest factor is the pull of the Moon and the Sun on the oceans. Generally, the Moon and Sun cause two high tides and two low tides. However, because the Moon takes 24 hours and 50 minutes to return to the same position above a given location, high tides and low tides occur about 50 minutes later each day. For example, if high tide at a location is at 10:00 AM one day, it will be at 10:50 AM the next day.

tide: the rise and fall of the surface level of a body of water due to the Moon's and the Sun's gravitational pull.

high tide: the time, for a certain location, when the tide is at its highest point.

low tide: the time, for a certain location, when the tide is at its lowest point.

High tide on left, low tide on right. Each occurs twice in a 24-hour period.

The Sun also has an influence on tides. Even though the Sun is farther away, it has much more mass than the Moon. If the Sun and the Moon are pulling in the same direction on Earth, when the three bodies are in a line, then the tides are stronger. If the Sun is pulling on Earth at a right angle from the Moon, then the tides are weaker.

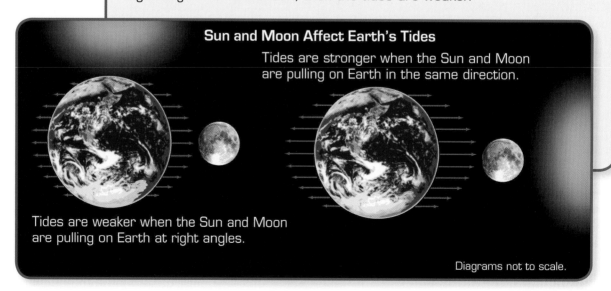

Sun and Moon Affect Earth's Tides

Tides are stronger when the Sun and Moon are pulling on Earth in the same direction.

Tides are weaker when the Sun and Moon are pulling on Earth at right angles.

Diagrams not to scale.

Learning Set 2

Back to the Big Question

How can you know if objects in space will collide?

In this *Learning Set,* you explored how Earth, the Moon, and the Sun interact. You learned that the Moon orbits Earth and Earth orbits the Sun. These orbits are predictable, so the location of each object in the solar system can be known to a high degree of accuracy. At the same time, each object is spinning on its axis. Because the rate that each object is spinning is also known, the way each object is oriented in space is also known to a high degree of accuracy.

By understanding the interactions and motions of the Earth-Moon-Sun system, you have an important building block in place for understanding the entire solar system. Return to your *Solar System* page and add the information you have learned about the characteristics and motions of the Moon, the Sun, and Earth.

Because Earth, the Moon, and the Sun move in predictable paths that do not intersect, they are not likely to collide with one another. However, the Moon may have had a central role in the largest collision in Earth's history.

A **theory** is a model or set of ideas used to explain how or why an event happens or happened. One question astronomers often ask is, *How did the Moon form?* Some astronomers believe that Earth and the Moon formed at the same time, when the entire solar system formed. In this theory, Earth and the Moon slowly collected debris that littered their orbit around the Sun. However, the theory accepted by most astronomers today is that the Moon's formation was more violent and dramatic.

Solar System 1.7.1/2.BBQ.2

Name: _____   Date: _____

Solar System Object	What characteristics does this object have?	How does this object move?
The Sun		
The Moon		
Inner Planets (Mercury, Venus, Earth, Mars)		
Outer planets (Jupiter, Saturn, Uranus, Neptune)		
Dwarf planets		
Asteroids, comets, meteoroids		
Other small solar-system bodies		

© It's About Time

You will see an animation that illustrates this theory. In this theory, Earth formed at the same time as the rest of the planets, and at first there was no Moon. Then, after the event described in the animation, the Moon formed. Watch the animation carefully. Write down any questions you have about what you saw.

Reflect

In your group, discuss the questions you had about the animation. Record any ideas you have that might answer the questions. Also record ways you could find out whether your ideas are correct. Use this opportunity to update your *Big Question* page. Add what you have learned about collisions from watching the animation.

Reflect

As a group, answer the following questions. When you are finished, choose one person from your group to read your answer aloud to the class. A different person should read the answer to each question.

Big Question			1.BBQ.1/2.BBQ.2
Name: _____		Date: _____	
How Can You Know if Objects in Space Will Collide?			
Type of Object	Evidence of Past Collisions	Chance of Future Collisions	What Would Happen?

© It's About Time

1. Describe the theory of the Moon's formation that is shown in the animation. How did scientists use computer models to test the theory?

2. In the theory presented in the animation, in what ways would material that makes up the Moon be the same as material that makes up Earth? In what ways might the material inside Earth and the Moon be different?

3. If the event that happened in the animation happened today, how would it affect life on Earth?

4. How did this animation change your understanding of collisions?

5. How is this theory a useful explanation for the formation of the Moon? Is there another possible theory for the formation of the Moon?

Communicate

Share Your Answers

Each group will share their answers to the *Reflect* questions. As you listen, take note of how the answers from other groups are the same as, and different from, your group's answers. Record things that you liked about other answers and things that you disagreed with. If you do not understand a group's presentation, ask questions. Make sure you ask respectfully. After all the groups have presented, the class will work together to reach agreement on an answer to each question. Record answers on a poster.

Revise Your Explanation

Now it is time to revise your explanation of how scientists can know if two space objects will collide. Use what you now know about gravity and the motion of Earth in the solar system to check the accuracy of what is in your first claim and explanation and to decide how to update them. Your earlier claim and explanation were about objects colliding with Earth. This time, revise your claim so that it is about how you can know if any two space objects will collide.

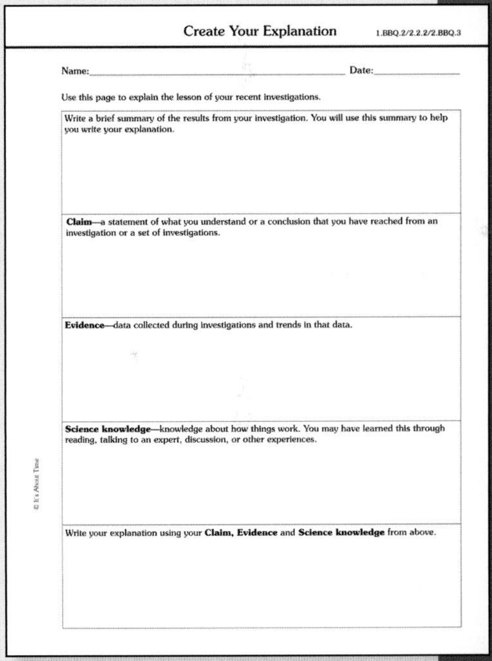
Create Your Explanation 1.BBQ.2/2.2.2/2.BBQ.3

Name:______________________ Date:__________

Use this page to explain the lesson of your recent investigations.

Write a brief summary of the results from your investigation. You will use this summary to help you write your explanation.

Claim—a statement of what you understand or a conclusion that you have reached from an investigation or a set of investigations.

Evidence—data collected during investigations and trends in that data.

Science knowledge—knowledge about how things work. You may have learned this through reading, talking to an expert, discussion, or other experiences.

Write your explanation using your **Claim, Evidence** and **Science knowledge** from above.

You have learned a lot more since you made your earlier claim and explanation, so you will probably want to use a new *Create Your Explanation* page for your revised explanation. Remember that a good explanation has several parts to it:

- **your claim:** a statement of what you understand or a conclusion you have reached
- **your evidence:** data collected from investigations that support your claim
- **your science knowledge:** knowledge about how things work that supports your claim
- **your explanation:** a logical statement connecting your evidence and science knowledge to your claim in a way that can convince someone that your claim is valid. Good explanations tell what is happening that makes the claim valid.

Your claim will be your clearest, most accurate statement about how you can know whether the space objects will collide. Your evidence comes from your investigations and your models of Earth, the Moon, and the Sun. Your science knowledge comes from your reading. Work to develop the best claim and explanation you can. It may be easier to express your explanation by attaching phrases to sketches than to simply use words. Feel free to combine sketches and words in your explanation.

Communicate

Share Your Explanation

Share your group's explanation with the rest of the class. As you are listening to the explanations of other groups, look for anything they have to say about determining whether two space objects will collide that you did not include in your explanation.

Reflect

With your partner, answer the following questions.

1. How trustworthy and complete do you think your explanation is?

2. What else do you need to investigate and learn about how the solar system moves to improve your explanation of how scientists can know if two space objects will collide.

Update the *Project Board*

Use the information that you added to your *Big Question* page and the information on the poster to update the *Project Board*. Concentrate on answering the questions you already have on the *Project Board* by adding information to the *What are we learning?* column, the *What is our evidence?* column, and the *What does it mean for the challenge or question?* column. You may wonder *Why do the planets move the way they do? How do other solar system objects they move?* Add these questions to the *What do we need to investigate?* column. You may also want to add other questions you have not answered but that you still need to answer.

Learning Set 3

How Do Other Solar-System Objects Move Through Space?

You have compared the sizes of Earth and the Moon, determined the distance between them, and explored how the motions of the Sun, Earth, and the Moon interact. However, if you want to make a prediction about which solar-system objects might collide with each other, you need to know about the rest of the objects in the solar system, how close they are to one another, and how they move. You probably already know something about the planets, but to answer the *Big Question,* you will need to know how far the planets are from each other and their relative sizes. You will also need to know why solar-system objects move the way they do. That will help you figure out how planets can affect the paths of space objects.

Pictured is an artist's illustration of the eight planets in the solar system, and the Moon. Scientists and students can make models of the solar system in many different ways.

One way to develop an understanding of the solar system is to build a model. Scientists use models to help them understand the solar system, and you will do the same thing. Like scientists, you may find that the process of building the model will give you a better understanding of the relationships and relative sizes of the planets.

orrery: a mechanical model of our solar system used to show the relative positions and movements of the planets.

scale model: a representation of an object that is related to the actual dimensions of the object by a fixed ratio.

Scientists and artists have been building models of our solar system for over two thousand years. Because our solar system is very complex, scientists have developed many different types of models. Each type allows them to explore different characteristics of the solar system.

One type of model scientists use to understand our solar system is called an **orrery**. An orrery is a model that shows the relative positions and motions of the planets. The first modern orrery was built in 1704. Like all models, an orrery represents our solar system well in some ways, but not in every way. While the orrery shows the motion of solar-system objects and how they may line up, it does not accurately show the sizes or distances between the objects. An orrery is a good tool for understanding how solar-system objects move, but for a better understanding of the chances of solar-system objects colliding, a model needs to show how big the objects are and the distances between them.

This orrery uses a crank handle and gears to move planets and the Moon in their orbits. The objects can spin and revolve.

Another type of model is a **scale model**. A scale model is a representation of an object related to the object's actual dimensions. You cannot go on a field trip to the planets, so the best way to understand how far the planets are from each other and how big they are is to build scale models. You will do that in this *Learning Set*. First you will build a scale model that shows the relative sizes and distances of the planets. Then you will use models to help you visualize the motions of the planets. You will also read about the orbits of planets and other solar-system objects and find out why objects travel in those orbits.

3.1 Understand the Question

Think About Making a Model of the Solar System

The *Big Question* for this Unit is *How can you know if objects in space will collide?* You know collisions occur because you have seen evidence of impacts. You also know the relationships among Earth, the Moon, and Sun. To make accurate predictions, it is necessary to know more about the other objects in the solar system and their motions.

One of the hardest things to understand about the solar system is how huge it is. You can start by visualizing its size this way. Think about getting from New York to Los Angeles. The driving distance from New York to Los Angeles is 4784 km (2973 mi). It would take about two days of driving day and night to get from one city to the other. That may seem like a great distance. However, it is only a small part of the distance it takes to go all the way around Earth. The distance around Earth at the Equator is called Earth's *circumference.* The circumference of Earth is more than eight times greater than the distance from New York to Los Angeles. If you could drive nonstop around the globe, it would take about 17 days. Other solar-system objects are larger than Earth, and the distances between solar-system objects are even greater. Earth is about 150 million kilometers from the Sun. This is 3733 times Earth's circumference. If you could drive to the Sun in a car, it would take you about 284 years to get there! Other planets are even farther from the Sun.

The circumference of Earth, measured around the Equator, is 40,075 km (24,901 mi). That is more than eight times greater than the distance from New York to Los Angeles.

ASTRONOMY

One way to better understand these sizes and distances is to make a scale model of the solar system. In this *Learning Set,* you will build a scale model of the Sun and the eight planets in the solar system. However, before you can begin building your model, you need to learn more about each of the objects that will be in your model.

Get Started

Each group in your class is going to become an expert on a different object in the solar system. Your model will have nine objects in it—the Sun and eight planets—so data for all nine objects are necessary to complete the model. Your teacher will tell you which object your group will investigate. Your solar-system object will either be the Sun or one of the seven planets other than Earth. As you gather information, remember that you will be responsible for teaching other groups about your solar-system object.

Procedure

1. Using available resources, gather the following information about the solar-system object assigned to your group. If your assigned object is the Sun, then some of the information does not apply.

   • size

   • mass

   • length of day (time to make one full revolution on its axis)

   • length of year (time to make one full orbit around the Sun)

   • composition

   • atmosphere

   • average distance from the Sun

   • similarities between your solar-system object and Earth or the Moon

   • differences between your solar-system object and Earth or the Moon

   • evidence of collisions between your solar-system object and other solar-system objects

- any other interesting information

2. After collecting your information, make a prediction among your group members about what you think would happen if an asteroid that is about 10 km (6 mi) across were to collide with your solar-system object. List your ideas and the supporting evidence. Your evidence may include what you have learned so far in this Unit.

3. Prepare a poster to share what you have learned with the class. Include a picture or sketch of your solar-system object, the information you gathered, and your answer to the question, *What would happen if a 10-km asteroid were to hit the solar-system object?* Make sure you include the evidence you used to answer this question. Be prepared to describe how your group reached this conclusion and why.

An artist imagines a collision of a huge asteroid with a planet such as Earth.

Communicate

Investigation Expo

When you have finished your investigation and prepared your poster, you will share what you learned with the class in an *Investigation Expo*. So that others will be able to learn from your work and use the information you present, you must clearly present what you know about your space object. Use your poster to guide your presentation. First, present the characteristics of your space object. Then present what you think would happen if a 10-km asteroid hit your space object. Support your answer with evidence.

As you listen to the presentations of other groups, make sure you understand what they are telling you about the characteristics of the space object they are reporting on. Ask questions if there is something you do not understand or if you think their information is incomplete. Also, be sure you agree with each group's answer to what would happen if a 10-km asteroid hit their space object. If you do not agree with their conclusion or you think their evidence did not fully support their answer, raise your hand and ask about their conclusions. Remember to be respectful. Here are some questions you might want to ask:

- How is your solar-system object similar to Earth or Earth's moon?

- How is your solar-system object different from Earth or Earth's moon?

- Describe any evidence that your object has ever been hit by another space object. What do you think happened?

- What was the most important evidence used to reach your conclusions?

Reflect

After listening to all of the presentations, you probably have a much better understanding of the planets that make up the solar system. Use what you have just heard to answer these questions.

1. What patterns do you see in the sizes of the planets?

2. What patterns do you see in the length of time it takes a planet to orbit the Sun?

Mercury, Venus, Earth, and Mars

3. Mercury, Venus, Earth, and Mars are different from Jupiter, Saturn, Uranus, and Neptune in several ways. Compare these two groups of planets. What similarities and differences do you find in the composition, atmosphere, and potential effect of collisions?

4. Your *Solar System* page divides the planets into two groups, the inner planets and the outer planets. Does this grouping make sense to you? What do you think the terms *inner planet* and *outer planet* refer to? What are other ways you could group the planets?

5. What else do you need to know to make a scale model of the solar system?

Update the *Project Board*

You have learned a lot about the Sun and the planets from the class presentations. Add to the *What do we think we know?* column the things you now know about how planets move around the Sun. Add to the *What do we need to investigate?* column any questions that you think need to be answered in order to accurately construct a scale model of the solar system or to predict collisions between solar-system objects.

What's the Point?

In this *Learning Set,* your goal is to gain a complete understanding of all of the components of the solar system. You have learned many facts about the planets from the presentations. In the rest of the *Learning Set* you will use this knowledge to make models that you can study to learn more about objects in the solar system and their motions.

Jupiter, Saturn, Uranus, and Neptune

3.2 Develop a Model

Choose Objects for a Model of the Solar System

Now that you know a little about the Sun and each of the planets in the solar system, you can begin to plan a scale model of the solar system. A scale model is a representation of an object or system that is larger, or smaller, than the actual size. This allows you to more easily study objects that are too small, too large, too far away, or too dangerous to study up close. The solar system is extremely large, so a scale model is a useful tool for studying its characteristics.

scale: the ratio of the distance between two points on a representation (such as a map or profile) and the actual distance between those two points.

scale factor: a ratio used to convert the actual sizes of an object to sizes in a model of that object.

You already know something about scale models. A map is a type of scale model because it is a different size than the area it represents. A well-drawn map allows you to compare distances from one place to another. A map also has a small bar on it that shows you how distances on the map compare to the actual distance on Earth's surface. This bar is called a **scale**, and the scale has a **scale factor**. A scale factor is a number used to convert from actual sizes to sizes that are used on the map. The scale might be stated in words. For example, the scale on the map might state a scale factor like this: 1 cm (0.4 in.) is equal to 10 km (6 mi). When the map was made, measurements of Earth's surface features were converted to map measurements using the scale factor. Each measurement was scaled down so that 1 centimeter on the map is equal to 10 kilometers on Earth. The map is much smaller than the actual area, but the map represents the area accurately because it is drawn to scale.

In this sample map, 2.1 cm equals 12 km, and 3.5 cm equals 12 miles.

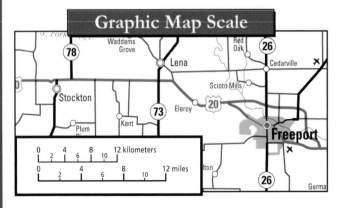

You will begin planning your solar-system model by thinking about a scale that could be used for the model. You know that the sizes of the planets vary. Some planets are smaller than Earth, and some are much larger. The distances between planets are much greater than the sizes of the planets. Determining the scale of a model can be difficult and requires you to think about how the model will be used.

For now, think only about the size of each of the solar-system objects—the Sun and the eight planets. Your job is to figure out what scale factor to use so that all of the objects in your model are able to fit in the classroom. For now, do not worry about how you will get objects through the door. Later, you will determine the distances between solar-system objects using the same scale.

Calculating Scale Factors: Can you Use an Apple to Represent Earth?

The first step in planning a scale model is to determine the scale factors you will use. One way to start is by choosing a model object that you could use to represent one object in the model. Then use calculations to see if the scale factor for this object will work for the other objects in your model. You will begin by calculating whether you can use an apple to represent Earth.

To determine whether an apple is a good size for Earth, you will first need to calculate the scale factor for using an apple to represent Earth. The procedure below shows you how to do that calculation, as well as how to calculate the diameter of a model Sun using the same scale factor. Follow the procedure, using a calculator to do the calculations on your own. Make sure your calculations match those in the procedure.

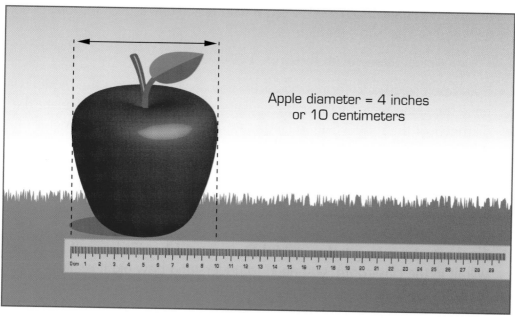

Apple diameter = 4 inches or 10 centimeters

Will this apple be the right size to represent Earth?

Procedure

1. **Determine the size of the model Earth.** The photograph shows an average-sized apple with a ruler next to it. The diameter of the apple in the picture is about 10 cm (4 in.).

2. **Compare the measurement of the model Earth with the actual Earth to get the scale factor.**

   Actual diameter of Earth: 12,756 km

   Diameter of the model Earth: 10 cm

   To find the ratio of the diameter of Earth to the diameter of the apple, you divide. This ratio, rounded to the nearest whole number, is the scale factor for the model.

   $$\frac{12{,}756 \text{ km}}{10 \text{ cm}} = \frac{1275.6 \text{ km}}{\text{cm}} \approx \frac{1276 \text{ km}}{\text{cm}}$$

   This means that 1 centimeter in the model represents an actual distance of 1276 kilometers. The scale factor can be written as follows:

   Scale: 1 cm = 1276 km

3. **Use the scale factor to find the diameter of the Sun in your model.** You can determine how big the other objects in your model would be using this scale. You begin with the actual size of the object you will model. The Sun's diameter is 1,392,000 km.

   Actual diameter of the Sun: 1,392,000 km

   If an apple is used to represent Earth, then every object in the model will have the same scale factor you calculated for the apple. To calculate the diameter of the model Sun in centimeters, divide the actual diameter of the Sun in kilometers by the scale factor.

   $$\begin{array}{cccc} 1{,}392{,}000 \text{ km} & \div & \frac{1276 \text{ km}}{\text{cm}} & = & 1091 \text{ cm} \\ \text{(diameter of the Sun)} & & \text{(scale factor)} & & \end{array}$$

   Diameter of the model Sun: 1091 cm

4. **Evaluate how large the model Sun would be.** To know if an object will fit in the classroom, you need to understand how big it really is. If an apple were used to model Earth, then the model Sun would have a diameter of 1091 centimeters. But how big is 1091 centimeters? If you convert 1091 cm into meters, you find that it is almost 11 m (36 ft).

Analyze Your Data

If you use an apple as your model Earth, will the other objects in your model solar system fit in your classroom? Answer these questions to decide.

Materials
• calculator

1. The diameter of the Sun in this model would be 11 m. What is about 11 m (36 ft) from where you are right now? It may help to think of the length of football field, which is 101 m (120 yd).

2. Think about how large your classroom is. Usually, the ceiling height in a classroom is about 2.75 m (9 ft). Will a ball that is 11 meters in diameter fit into your classroom?

3. In order for every object in the solar system to be small enough to fit into the classroom, does Earth have to be smaller or larger than the size of an apple? What other objects do you think you could you use to represent Earth?

4. What procedure will you follow to determine if the object you choose will be a good model for Earth? Which space objects would you have to calculate the sizes of to decide that? Why?

Can You Use a Peppercorn to Represent Earth?

When Earth is represented in your model by an apple, the model Sun is too big to fit into a classroom. A peppercorn is much smaller than an apple and might be a better object to represent Earth. A peppercorn is tiny compared to the apple, with a diameter of only 0.2 cm. To determine if a peppercorn is a good size for your model Earth, you must repeat the same calculations you did for the apple. Follow the procedure below, using a calculator to make your own calculations. Make sure your calculations match those in the procedure.

Procedure

1. **Determine the size of the model Earth.** The photograph on right shows average-sized peppercorns. Measure the diameter of one peppercorn. You should find that it is about 0.2 cm.

Could one of these peppercorns be your model Earth?

2. **Compare the measurement of the model Earth with the actual Earth to get the scale factor.**

Actual diameter of Earth: 12,756 km

Diameter of the model Earth: 0.2 cm

To find the scale factor, divide the actual diameter of Earth by the diameter of your model Earth.

$$12{,}756 \text{ km} \div 0.2 \text{ km} \approx \frac{63{,}780 \text{ km}}{\text{cm}}$$

This means that 1 centimeter in the model represents an actual distance of 63,780 kilometers. That is the scale factor for this model.

Scale: 1 cm = 63,780 km

3. **Use the scale factor to find the diameter of the Sun in your model.** You begin with the actual size of the object you will model.

Actual diameter of the Sun: 1,392,000 km

If a peppercorn is used to represent Earth, then every object in the model will have to use the same scale factor you calculated for the peppercorn. To calculate the diameter of the model Sun in centimeters, divide the actual diameter of the Sun in kilometers by the scale factor.

$$\underset{\text{(diameter of the Sun)}}{1{,}392{,}000 \text{ km}} \quad \div \quad \underset{\text{(scale factor)}}{\frac{63{,}780 \text{ km}}{\text{cm}}} \quad \approx \quad 22 \text{ cm}$$

Diameter of the model Sun: 22 cm

This model Sun is much smaller than the one you had when using an apple to represent Earth.

Stop and Think

1. How big is 22 centimeters? There are 2.54 centimeters in an inch. Figure out how big 22 centimeters is. Then list three spherical objects that are about that big.

2. What object might you use to represent the Sun if it needs to be about 22 centimeters in diameter?

Choose Model Objects to Represent the Sun and Planets

Your class will construct a model of the solar system using a peppercorn as a model Earth. You have already calculated the scale factor for Earth in this model. Now you will choose objects to represent the other objects in the solar system. Each must be chosen using the scale factor you chose for Earth. In the last section, each group became an expert on the characteristics of a planet or the Sun. Now you will work with your group to find an object of the correct size to represent your solar-system object in the class model of the solar system.

Procedure

1. Record the scale factor at the top of your *Solar-System Model* page.

2. In the table, find the row for your solar-system object. In this row, record the actual diameter of your solar-system object in the *Diameter* column.

3. Use the scale factor to calculate the diameter of your model object in centimeters. Record this measurement in the *Diameter of the model object* column.

4. Find a round object that is about that size. If possible, choose an object that is available in your classroom. Record the name of your object in the *Model object that is the correct size* column.

5. Now, use the scale factor to calculate the distance your object is from the Sun. First, record the average actual distance your object is from the Sun in the *Average distance from the Sun* column. Then calculate the distance your model object should be from the model Sun. Use the formula

$$\frac{\text{Actual distance from Sun}}{\text{Scale factor}} = \text{Distance from model Sun}$$

Solar System Model 3.2.1

Name: _____ Date: _____

Scale 1 cm = _____ km

Solar-system object	Diameter (km)	Diameter of the model object (cm)	Model object that is the correct size	Average distance from the Sun (km)	Distance from the model Sun (cm)	Paces from the model Sun
Sun						
Mercury						
Venus						
Earth						
Mars						
Jupiter						
Saturn						
Uranus						
Neptune						

© It's About Time

Communicate

Share Your Data

When it is your group's turn to present, share your data with the class, and record your data on a large class *Solar-System Model* page so that everyone can see it. Each member of the class should also complete their own *Solar-System Model* page. Everyone in the class will need to have their own set of data for the next activity.

Analyze Your Data

1. Which is the smallest solar-system object? How much smaller is it than Earth?

2. Which is the largest solar-system object? How much larger is it than Earth?

3. What surprised you about the sizes of the everyday objects you are using to represent the Sun and planets?

4. Look carefully at the column that shows the average distance from the Sun. Use what you know about the sizes of objects you are familiar with to visualize how far the planets will be from each other in a scale model of the orbits. How far do you think it will be from the model Sun to the model Mercury (the first planet from the Sun)? How far do you think your group's model solar-system object will be from the model Sun? How do you think you can represent these distances?

5. Now assume that you will be walking the distance between model objects using large paces. Assume that one pace is 1 meter. Divide the model distance (in cm) between your planet and the Sun by 100. This will tell you about how many paces it would take to walk from the model Sun to your model planet.

6. Record the number of paces from the model Sun to your model planet in the last column of the class *Solar-System Model* page.

Reflect

1. Record the distance in paces from the Sun to each planet on your *Solar-System Model* page.

2. Calculate the distance in paces from your planet to the two closest planets. Be prepared to share your data with the class.

3. What, if anything, surprises you about the distances from the Sun to the planets or from your planet to the two closest planets?

Walk Your Model

How Much Space Do You Need?

You will have to take a long walk to model the distances from the Sun to the planets. Take your *Solar-System Model* page with you for the walk, and take your group's model solar-system object. Your teacher will take the model Earth. Your class will begin the walk together. You will stop when you have paced off the correct model distance for each planet. You will place the model objects on the ground at those places and then walk with the teacher to the next planet.

Materials

• model solar-system objects

• completed *Solar-System Model* page

Procedure

1. First, go to the place your teacher tells you is the location of the model Sun. Place the object that represents the Sun on the ground.

2. Your teacher will now walk away from the Sun and call out distances in meters. Walk with the teacher. When you reach the correct model distance for your planet, call out to the class "[my planet] is here!" Then put your model planet on the ground. For example, the first group to reach its planet's orbit will be the Mercury group. The Mercury group should say "Mercury is here!" and then put their model Mercury on the ground.

3. At each place you stop, look back at the other objects. Notice how far away you are getting from the Sun and the other planets.

4. The teacher will then continue walking and calling out distances from the Sun. Continue to mark the position of each planet until all eight planets have been marked or until you run out of time. If you complete your scale model of the solar system, look back at the whole model from Neptune's position. Notice how far you have gone!

5. When you are finished, collect the solar-system objects and return to the classroom. Be sure to follow the teacher's instructions.

The actual diameter of the Sun is 1,392,000 km; the actual diameter of Earth is 12,756 km.

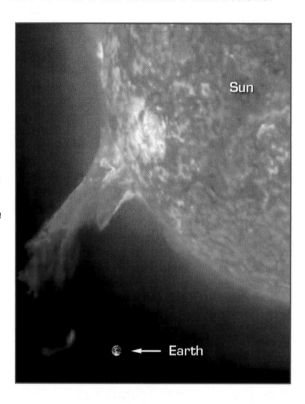

Reflect

1. How did the distances from the model Sun to the model planets compare to the sizes of the model planets?

2. How did the model help you to understand the distances between solar-system objects?

3. When you stood at Neptune, or the last planet you marked, and looked back at the rest of your solar-system model, how much of the model could you see?

4. Suppose you wanted to make a new model with the goal of fitting the orbits of *every* planet within your classroom. What do you think the sizes of the planets and the Sun in such a model would be?

5. Do you think that planets in our solar system can collide with each other? Why or why not? What would you need to know to know to determine whether your answer to this question is correct?

Measuring Long Distances

As you saw from building your model, the distances from the Sun to the farthest planets are very large. For example, Neptune is nearly 4.5 billion kilometers from the Sun. Because those distances are so large, instead of expressing them in kilometers, astronomers have defined a different unit that they use to describe distances in the solar system. Remember that the average distance from Earth to the Sun is about 150 million kilometers (93 million miles). Astronomers define this distance as 1 **astronomical unit (AU)**. They then use this unit to express other distances in space. When they measure in astronomical units, they are comparing all other distances to the distance between the Sun and Earth. For example, the distance from Mars to the Sun is about 1.5 AU, or about 1.5 times the distance from Earth to the Sun. And Neptune is about 30 AU from the Sun. That means it is 30 times farther from the Sun than Earth is. The number 30 is easier to grasp than 4.5 billion!

astronomical unit (AU): a measure of distance based on Earth's orbit. One AU is equal to the average distance of Earth from the Sun, about 150 million kilometers.

Update the *Project Board*

You have just experienced the relative sizes of the Sun and planets in the solar system and their relative distances from each other and from the Sun. You might have been amazed at the vast distance that the solar system occupies. The scale of the solar system has important consequences for your prediction of whether objects will collide with Earth. Fill in the *What are we learning?* and *What is our evidence?* columns of the *Project Board* with the insights you have gained from making a solar-system model. Then add new questions you have generated to the *What do we need to investigate?* column.

What's the Point?

A scale model can be constructed using a scale factor. The scale factor is a ratio that relates actual distances to distances in the model. You can find a scale factor using one object in a model. In a model of the solar system, you first find the scale factor for one object, such as Earth. You then use the scale factor to find the size of each model object. The scale factor also is used to calculate the distance between model objects. In a solar-system model, it helps to find the model size of the largest object, the Sun, to make sure the model will not be too large.

No model can perfectly represent all features. Your model represented the sizes of the objects and the distances between the objects accurately. However, this meant the model planets had to be far from the model Sun. This made it difficult to visualize the entire model at once.

The actual distances to planets are large numbers when measured in kilometers. Astronomers use a unit called the astronomical unit (AU) to measure distances in the solar system. The astronomical unit is defined as the average distance from Earth to the Sun, which is about 150 million kilometers.

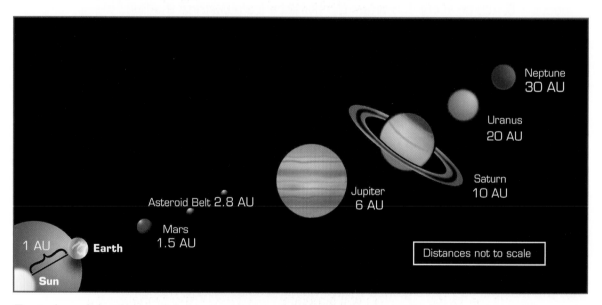

To study and develop models in astronomy, scientists need to quantify distances that are unimaginable. The approximate distance of 150 million kilometers between Earth and the Sun is 1 astronomical unit.

3.3 Explore

How Can You Predict the Locations of the Planets?

In the model your class just made, you walked off the distances to each of the planets starting from the Sun. The distances in the model probably were greater than you thought they would be.

Your final model was laid out in a straight line. Think about the amount of space you would need if you wanted to show how the planets actually orbit the Sun!

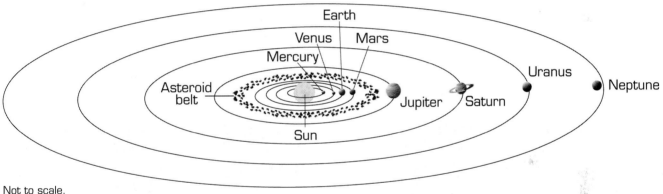

Not to scale.

Can the planets collide with each other? You can only know the answer to this question if you know how the planets move in relation to each other. You know that the planets orbit the Sun, but you may not know exactly how close they get to each other or what their orbits look like. To find out whether the planets can collide with each other, you need to know these things.

In *Learning Set 2*, you learned that Earth orbits the Sun. The other planets also orbit the Sun. Each planet orbits the Sun in a path that is nearly circular. In this *Learning Set*, you will simulate the orbits of the planets. You will have a chance to see how the planets move around the Sun in relation to one another.

Build a Moving Model of the Solar System

A moving model, or simulation, of the solar system will show you the orbits of various planets compared to each other. However, to make a simulation in which you can see the relative motion of the planets, you will have to make some adjustments to the model you have been using. The model will not be to scale for size or distance. Also, it will be easier to visualize if the number of solar-system objects is limited to six—the Sun, Mercury, Venus, Earth, Mars, and Jupiter. Six students in the class will represent the Sun and planets. The rest of the class should watch carefully and offer advice as the six students set themselves up. Then the class should watch as the Sun and planets carry out the simulation.

Set Up the Model

period (of an orbiting object): the time it takes an object to complete one revolution around another space object.

1. Begin by positioning a person representing the Sun in the middle of the space you are using for your model. Use a large enough space to allow five students to move in circular orbits about the Sun.

2. Arrange five students in a straight line out from the Sun, at about equal distance from each other. Remember that you are not using an accurate distance scale for this model.

3. In this simulation, Earth is the planet in the middle. Earth will take one minute to go around the Sun. The student who is representing Earth should practice walking one quarter of the way around the Sun in 15 seconds. Another student should act as a clock and count off seconds.

4. The time it takes a planet to move around the Sun is called its **period**. Mercury and Venus will move faster than Earth, while Mars and Jupiter will move more slowly than Earth. Using the numbers on the table as a guide, calculate how much time each model planet will take to travel one quarter of its orbit around the Sun. Enter these values in the last row of the table.

5. Each person representing a planet should practice walking his or her orbit at the correct speed. Someone will need to count off seconds. To learn how fast to walk, practice walking one quarter of the orbit in the time calculated in the last row of the table.

	Mercury	Venus	Earth	Mars	Jupiter
Orbital period (in Earth years)	0.24 years	0.62 years	1 year	1.88 years	11.86 years
Orbital period in model (1 Earth year = 1 minute)	14 seconds	37 seconds	60 seconds	109 seconds	712 seconds
One-quarter of orbital period in model			15 seconds		

Simulate the Movement of the Planets

1. All model planets should start in a straight line. Someone should act as a clock.

2. Begin the simulation. The clock should count out seconds. Each student should be careful to walk at the correct speed around the Sun. Model planets should try to observe the motion of the other planets as they walk.

3. Every minute, when Earth is back to the beginning of its orbit, pause the simulation. All the model planets should stop. Check where the other planets are. Use tape to mark the spot on the floor where each planet is after every Earth year. Label each piece of tape with the planet's name and the number of the Earth year at which the position was marked.

4. Repeat for 10 Earth years.

Analyze Your Data

After running the simulation, work together to analyze the data from the simulation. These questions will help you analyze the data. The first two questions are specific to a particular planet and require information from the person representing that planet. Other questions are for the rest of the class to answer.

1. How did the motion of the other planets appear from Mercury?

2. How did the motion of the other planets appear from Jupiter?

3. Mercury and Venus have orbital periods that are shorter than Earth's. How must they move, compared to Earth, to simulate the orbits correctly?

ASTRONOMY

4. Jupiter is farther from the Sun than Earth. Jupiter's speed is slower than Earth's speed. How many times does Earth orbit the Sun in the time it takes Jupiter to orbit the Sun?

gravity: the force of attraction between two objects due to their mass; the greater the mass in each object, the stronger the attraction; the more distance between the objects, the weaker the attraction.

universe: everything that exists, including all objects in space.

Why Do Planets Orbit the Sun?

When you drop a ball, it falls to Earth. You can predict that the ball will fall every time. On Earth this is what you have learned to expect. The ball falls because the ball and Earth are attracted to each other. This attraction is called **gravity**, and it happens between every object in the **universe**, not just balls or other falling objects and Earth.

Two factors determine the strength of the force of gravity that two objects exert on each other. If the mass of either object increases, the attraction between the objects increases. But as the distance between two objects increases, the attraction between them decreases.

The Sun and all the planets are attracted to each other. As you know, the Sun has much more mass than any planet. Therefore, the Sun pulls on each planet more strongly than the planets pull on each other.

If the Sun is pulling all of the planets toward it, why do the planets remain in their orbits? What keeps the planets from falling into the Sun? Any object in motion has a tendency to resist any change in its motion. An object will keep moving in a straight line unless something causes it to change its motion. This means that a planet would continue to move in a straight line off into space unless a force acted on it to change its motion. In the solar system there is a force acting on the planet. The gravitational attraction between the planet and the Sun pulls the planet toward the Sun. As a result of gravity, planets move around the Sun instead of continuing off into space in a straight line.

Think about spinning a ball on a string above your head. As you spin the ball, it is being pulled toward you by the string. You are applying a force to hold the string. This force is directed toward you. The force on the string is similar to the force of gravity pulling a planet toward the Sun. If you let go of the string, the ball will fly off in a straight line. The force of the string that pulls the ball toward you is the force that changes the straight-line motion of the ball. When that force is removed, the ball is free to travel in a straight line.

Gravity is also the force responsible for the orbits of moons around the planets. For example, the Moon orbits Earth because of the gravitational attraction between Earth and the Moon. But why does the Moon orbit Earth when Earth has so much less mass than the Sun? Remember that distance also affects the strength of gravity's force of attraction. The Moon is much closer to Earth than to the Sun, so the gravitational pull from Earth is strong enough to pull the Moon into orbit around Earth.

Because the attractions among the planets are small compared to the Sun's gravity, the orbits of the planets stay the same for very long periods of time. However, a gravitational tug from a large planet such as Jupiter can significantly change the orbit of an asteroid or a comet. For this reason, the orbits of small objects can change over time, and they must be tracked closely to be able to predict where they will be at any given time.

Imagine spinning a ball on a string above your head. The ball is being pulled toward you the way gravity pulls a planet toward the Sun.

Reflect

1. On Earth, a **year** is equal to 365.25 days, or about 12 months. This is how long it takes Earth to orbit the Sun. Scientists define a year as the time it takes a planet to orbit the Sun. This means that the length of a year is different for *every* planet. What do you notice about the orbital periods, or years, of the planets between the Sun and Earth compared to those beyond Earth?

   year: the time it takes for a solar-system object to make one complete revolution around the Sun.

2. Eris is a dwarf planet farther away from the Sun than Neptune. Its average distance is about 100 AU from the Sun. Using what you have learned from the simulation, how do you think the orbital period of Eris would compare to those of Earth and Jupiter?

3. What do you think would happen to Jupiter's orbit if Jupiter were to replace Earth at a distance of 1 AU from the Sun?

4. Jupiter orbits the Sun at a distance of about 5 AU, and Saturn orbits the Sun at a distance of about 10 AU. Compare the likelihood of the following objects colliding with either Jupiter or Saturn:

   a) a meteoroid with a circular orbit at a distance of 7 AU from the Sun

   b) a meteoroid with an elliptical orbit that varies from 4 AU to 15 AU from the Sun

elliptical orbit: an orbit in the shape of a flattened circle (ellipse).

ellipse: a shape that is a squashed or flattened circle. The sum of the distances from a point on the ellipse to each of the two foci is the same for every point on the ellipse.

eccentricity: a measurement used to describe the shape of an ellipse.

focus (plural, foci): one of two fixed points that determine the shape of an ellipse.

The Shape of Planetary Orbits

In your simulation, you moved in nearly circular orbits around the Sun. And what you just read about gravity tells you that the orbits of planets could be circular, just like when you spin a ball above your head on a string. However, no perfectly circular solar-system orbits have been discovered.

If the orbits of planets are not in the shape of a circle, what shape are they? Each planet moves around the Sun in an **elliptical orbit**. An elliptical orbit is in the shape of an **ellipse**. You can think of an ellipse as a "squashed" or flattened circle. The degree to which an ellipse appears flattened is described by a number called its **eccentricity**. The eccentricity of an ellipse is a number between 0 and 1 that tells how different the shape of an ellipse is from a circle. The closer the shape is to a circle, the lower the eccentricity. The eccentricity of a circle is 0. It is not flattened at all. Eccentricities that are close to 1 describe ellipses that are very stretched out. Earth's orbit has an eccentricity of 0.0167, which is very close to 0. Some solar-system objects, such as comets, can have elongated orbits with eccentricities close to 1.

If a planet's orbit were a perfect circle, the Sun would sit right in the center of the circle. Every point on the orbit would be the same distance from the Sun. Instead of a center, ellipses have two **foci**. (Note that foci is the plural form of **focus**.) For any point on an elliptical orbit, the sum of the distances from the point to the two foci is always the same. You can draw an ellipse using two pushpins, a loop of string, and a pencil as shown. The farther apart you make the two foci, the more stretched out the ellipse is.

All of the objects going around the Sun have elliptical orbits. In each case, the Sun is located at one focus of the orbit. For example, think about Earth's orbit. Because the orbit is nearly circular, the foci are very close together. At the closest point to the Sun in its orbit, Earth is 147 million kilometers from the Sun. At the farthest point in its orbit, Earth is 152 million kilometers from the Sun. A difference of 5 million kilometers may seem like a lot, but it is a small fraction of the total distance between Earth and the Sun. You might think it would be warmer on Earth when it is closer to the Sun, but in fact Earth is farthest from the Sun in July, when it is summer in the Northern hemisphere.

The orbits of the planets are nearly circular, but objects like comets and asteroids can have flattened orbits. This means that the foci are farther apart. For these orbits, the distance between the object and the Sun changes a great deal throughout the orbit.

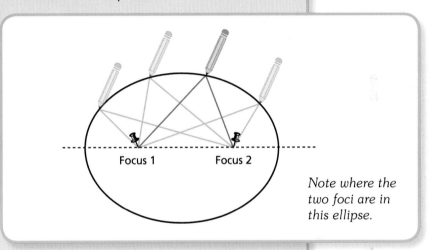

Note where the two foci are in this ellipse.

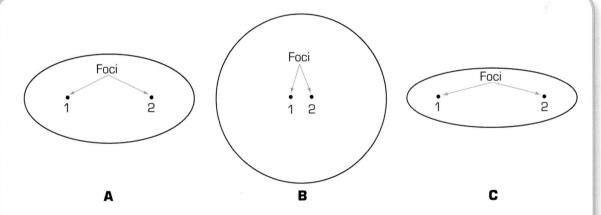

A   B   C

The more flattened the ellipse, the greater its eccentricity. Earth's orbit is almost circular, so the foci are very close together. Which of the ellipses pictured is the most eccentric? Which one is the least?

PBIS

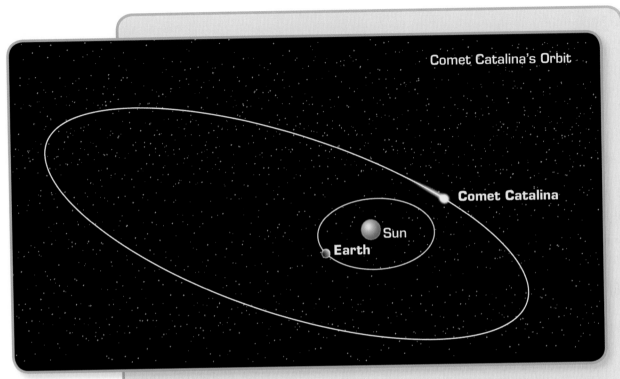

Comet Catalina's Orbit

Comet Catalina

Sun

Earth

Earth has an eccentricity of close to 0. Its orbit is a rounded ellipse, almost a circle. The comet Catalina has an eccentricity of 0.5. Notice how different the two orbits are. Not to scale.

Stop and Think

1. Which objects in the solar system have nearly circular orbits? Which objects have orbits that are more flattened ellipses?

2. Do you think collisions between a planet and an asteroid would be more likely if the asteroid's orbit is a more circular ellipse or a more flattened ellipse? Why?

3. You have read that the orbit of a small solar-system object can change over time. How would you describe the changes that could occur in the shape of the orbit?

4. An orbit in two dimensions is described by the average distance from the Sun and the eccentricity of the orbit. What other factor can you think of that might be used to describe an orbit in three dimensions? How do you think this factor affects the likelihood of collision with another solar-system object?

Update the *Project Board*

So far in this *Learning Set* you have considered the sizes of several solar-system objects and the distance of these objects from the Sun. You learned about the shape of orbits and simulated how several planets orbit the Sun. This is all important information that will be needed to answer the *Big Question* for the Unit and should now be added to the *Project Board*.

Record your ideas about the motions of solar-system objects in the *What are we learning?* and *What is our evidence?* columns. Record any questions you still have or things you need to investigate further to predict when collisions between space objects may occur under *What do we need to investigate?* You will learn more about objects in the solar system and answer many of your questions during the rest of the *Learning Set*.

What's the Point?

Solar-system objects that orbit the Sun move in elliptical orbits. The shape of these orbits may be close to a perfect circle or may be more flattened in shape. Scientists describe the shape of elliptical orbits by measuring their eccentricities. An ellipse with an eccentricity close to 0 is nearly circular, and an ellipse with an eccentricity close to 1 is elongated.

Planets close to the Sun take less time to orbit the Sun than Earth, while the planets farther from the Sun take more time to orbit the Sun. The time it takes each object to make one full trip around the Sun is a year. This means a year for Venus is shorter than an Earth year, while a year for Mars is longer than an Earth year.

Two factors account for planets and other solar-system objects remaining in their orbits. One factor is the tendency of an object in motion to remain in motion in a straight line unless acted on by another force. Gravity is the second factor that accounts for solar-system objects remaining in their orbits. Gravitational attraction between the Sun and each solar-system object bends the object's path into an elliptical orbit.

PBIS

3.4 Explore

What Do Moving Planets Look Like From Earth?

In *Learning Set 2,* you saw how difficult it was to determine the real motion of objects in the solar system simply by observing what was seen in the sky. However, in *Learning Set 2,* you only had to deal with two objects in the sky, the Sun and the Moon. Now imagine how difficult the problem becomes when you consider all of the planets.

You also learned that the stars rise and set each night, but that they stay fixed in relation to one another. Long ago, observers named patterns they see in the stars. These patterns are called *constellations.*

Oct 12   Oct 7   Oct 3   Sept 27   Sept 19   Sept 14   Sept 8   Sept 1   Aug 28   Aug 23   Aug 21

Early astronomers noticed the movement of planets across the sky. In this composite image, Mars is seen moving to the left over the course of about two months.

Early astronomers used the fixed background of stars to track the motions of the Sun, the Moon, and the planets. They noticed that a few bright star-like objects moved slowly in different paths across the sky and seemed to "wander" among the stars. At times, these objects even seemed to reverse their direction against the background. The word "planet" comes from a Greek word meaning "wanderer." The Greeks gave these objects this name because the planets did not remain fixed like the stars.

AST 142

In the last section, you ran a simulation of five planets orbiting the Sun. This model showed the motion of the planets as though you were observing from outside the solar system. The model worked well to compare the rates at which each planet orbits the Sun. However, the model did not represent the relative positions of the planets as you see them from Earth. Now, you will see what the moving planets look like from Earth and, like the ancient astronomers, you will learn to predict their movements.

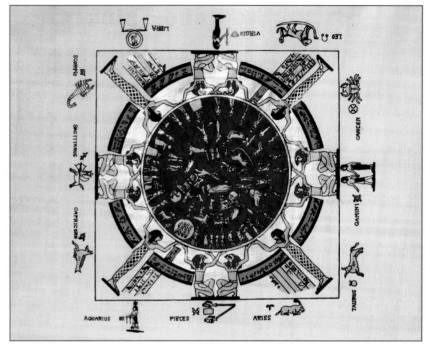

The ancient Egyptians based their calendars on observations of the stars. Around the outside edge of the Egyptian calendar pictured are 12 star constellations, each representing a period of about 30 days

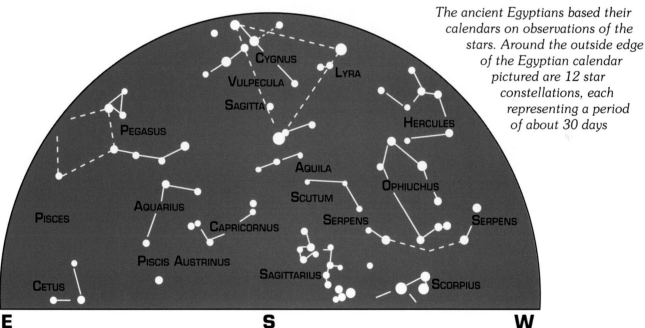

E　　　　　　　**S**　　　　　　　**W**

Stars stay fixed in relation to one another. The patterns that they form have been observed by people since ancient times. They named some of these patterns "constellations."

Stop and Think

1. How did the motions of the planets look when viewed from outside of the solar system? How do you think your view of the motions of the planets would change if you viewed them from Earth?

2. Describe how early astronomers might have used a background of stars to identify planets.

Simulating Motions of the Planets

Knowing the positions of the planets, and being able to predict where they will be in the future, would be important to anyone trying to predict if, and when, objects in the solar system might collide. In this activity, you will use the model on the *Planetary Orbit Simulation* chart, which shows the orbits of five planets. This model also includes the Sun and 12 constellations. These constellations can be thought of as landmarks in the sky, against which you can compare the movements of the planets. Using this representation, you will work with a model of the planets as they are seen from Earth. You will record your observations on the *Planetary Orbit Observations* page.

Chinese astronomers are believed to have been the first to map the position of the stars, as seen in this map from 4 B.C.E.

Materials

• ruler
• pencil
• *Planetary Orbit Observations* page
• *Planetary Orbit Simulation* chart

Procedure

1. Examine the model on the *Planetary Orbit Simulation* chart. Find the orbits of Mercury, Venus, Earth, Mars, and Jupiter. Review the model with your group.

   a) Locate the Sun.

   b) Locate the 12 constellations.

   c) Locate the numbered positions of the five planets.

Project-Based Inquiry Science

2. Find position 1 for each planet. This represents where each planet is in the month of January in a particular year.

3. Determine which constellation is seen behind Mercury when observed from Earth in January. To do this, line up Earth in position 1 with Mercury in position 1, continuing the line to the constellations in the outer circle. This is the constellation that would appear behind Mercury as seen from Earth in January. Record the name of the constellation in the January row of the table on the *Planetary Orbit Observations* page.

4. Using the same procedure as you used in Step 3, record the constellations behind Venus, Mars, Jupiter, and the Sun as seen from Earth in January. For the Sun, you will not need to find a position number because the Sun does not change its position.

Planetary Orbit Observations 3.4.2

Name: _____ Date: _____

Month	Constellation behind Sun	Constellation appearing behind the planet			
		Mercury	Venus	Mars	Jupiter
January					
February					
March					
April					
May					
June					
July					
August					
September					
October					
November					
December					

© It's About Time

5. After one month, each planet will be in position 2. Using the same procedure you used in Step 3, observe which constellation is behind each planet and the Sun in February. This time, however, make your observations using position 2 for each planet. Record the names of the constellations in the February row of the table on the *Planetary Orbit Observations* page.

6. Continue making observations for the Sun and each planet one month at a time. After position 3, you will need to add in position numbers for each planet. For Mercury, position 4 will be the same as position 1, position 5 will be the same as position 2, and so on. Record the background constellations on the *Planetary Orbit Observations* page.

PBIS

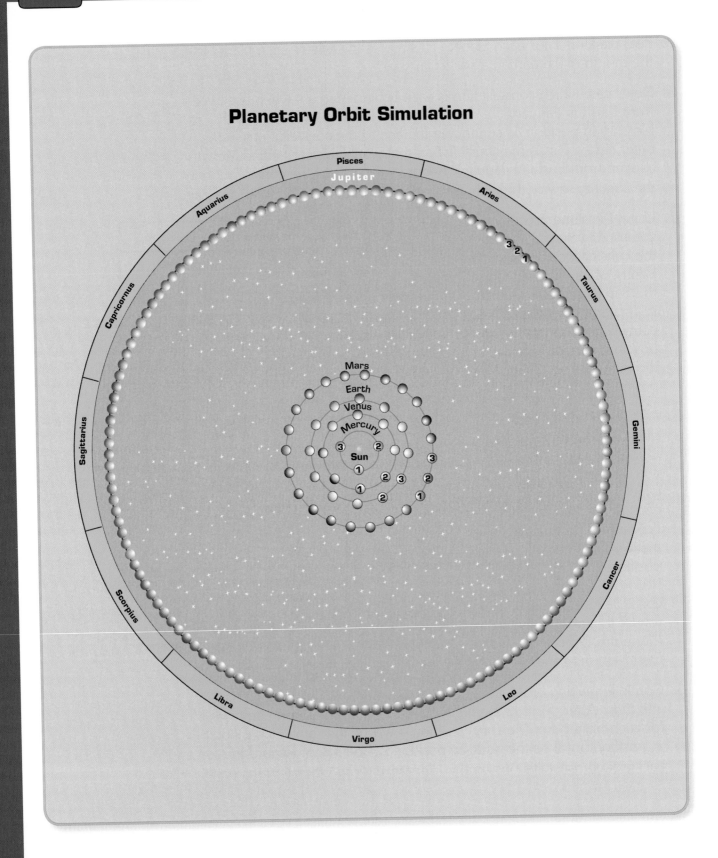

Planetary Orbit Simulation

Analyze Your Data

1. Describe any patterns or trends you were able to identify in the movements of the five planets as seen from Earth.

2. How did the position of Mercury in each month compare with the position of the Sun? How did the position of Venus in each month compare with the position of the Sun?

3. By studying the *Planetary Orbit Simulation* page and your data, describe when and where in the night sky you should look if you want to find Mercury or Venus. (Caution: Do not attempt to observe these planets without first discussing safety issues with your teacher.)

4. How does the Sun progress through the constellations throughout the year? In which direction around the circle does the Sun's background constellation move, clockwise or counterclockwise? In which direction do the background constellations for Mercury and Venus move?

5. What, if any, is the relationship between the locations of Mars and Jupiter and the position of the Sun?

6. What did you notice about the pattern of background constellations for Mars and Jupiter?

Determining the Structure of the Solar System

The simulation you just used made it very clear that the motion of the planets as seen from Earth is confusing. However, you have already learned that the planets move in nearly circular orbits around the Sun. Ancient astronomers had to figure this out for themselves. Astronomers have been able to accurately predict the position of the planets in the sky for over two thousand years. But, the correct model for the solar system was not agreed upon until the 1600s.

A good model of the solar system must account for many observations. One of the most difficult observations to represent in a solar-system model is **retrograde motion**. In general, the planets move across the sky from west to east against the background of fixed stars. During retrograde motion, planets such as Mars and Jupiter appear to reverse direction and travel east to west. You observed the retrograde motion of Mars and Jupiter on the *Planetary Orbit Simulation* page.

retrograde motion: motion of an outer planet in which the planet appears to reverse direction as seen from Earth.

All of the solar-system models you have seen show the Sun at the center of the planets. The Sun is the largest object in the solar system and the planets and other solar-system objects move around it. Although this is what you have been taught, and this is now accepted as a fact, people did not always know this.

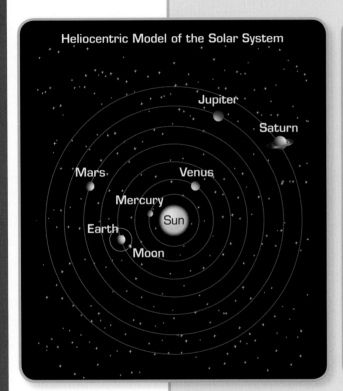

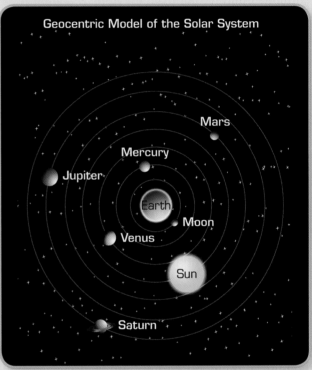

Astronomers in many cultures have made observations of the sky for thousands of years, but the Greeks are credited with developing astronomy as a science. The early Greeks also, quite possibly, set the stage for a long debate about the structure of the solar system. Most early astronomers made the assumption that Earth was the center of the universe. This was an easy mistake to make, because Earth does not feel like it is moving, and objects in the sky seem to circle around Earth as it spins. In 280 B.C.E., the Greek astronomer Aristarchus developed a model of the solar system, called a **heliocentric** model, with the Sun at the center. However, his model was largely ignored.

About 400 years later, another influential Greek astronomer, Claudius Ptolemy, developed a model with Earth at the center of the solar system. A model with Earth at its center is called a **geocentric** model. While this

heliocentric: model of the solar system in which the Sun is at the center.

geocentric: model of the solar system in which Earth is at the center.

geocentric model allowed Ptolemy to accurately predict the positions of the planets, it relied on some complex details to predict retrograde motion of a planet like Mars. Ptolemy's model also included some slight imperfections in the calculations. Despite these imperfections, Ptolemy's model remained widely accepted until the 1500s because it could be used to accurately predict positions of the planets in the sky. In 1473, the Polish astronomer Nicolaus Copernicus worked to improve on Ptolemy's geocentric model. He found that a much simpler model is possible when the Sun is the center of the solar system. His heliocentric model could explain retrograde motion by showing the relative motion of the faster-moving Earth as it passes a slower-moving outer planet. But the heliocentric model of Copernicus also had imperfections and in fact it was no better than Ptolemy's model in predicting the motions of the planets. Yet the Copernicus model got scientists thinking about the solar system in a different way.

The debate about the two models continued for more than a century. Finally, in 1609, Galileo started using the newly invented telescope to make observations. His data supported the heliocentric model.

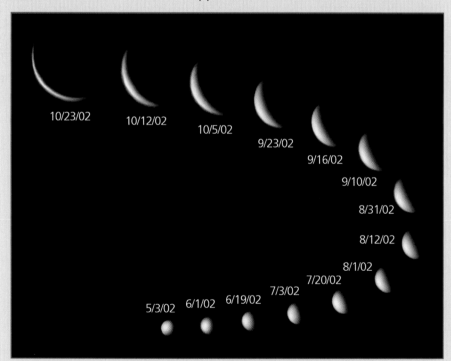

Galileo demonstrated that from Earth, Venus can be seen in all its phases. This confirmed that Venus orbited the Sun, not the Earth.

Largely for religious reasons, it was many years before Galileo's observations were accepted. At the time, people preferred a universe with Earth at its center. But finally, scientific thinking triumphed, and the heliocentric model of the solar system was accepted.

It took nearly 2000 years for people to move from first recognizing the difference between stars and planets to showing that Earth orbits the Sun. At about the same time that the heliocentric model was finally accepted, astronomers also figured out the elliptical nature of the orbits. It was the assumption Copernicus made that the orbits of the planets were circular that caused the imperfections in his model.

In the 16th century, Danish astronomer Tycho Brahe made even more accurate observations. He insisted that nightly observations be made at his observatory. He wrote his observations and data analyses in several books. From these exact observations, Brahe's assistant, Johannes Kepler, a German astronomer and mathematician, studied and analyzed the heliocentric model of Copernicus.

By 1609, Kepler had developed three laws of planetary motion. In these laws, Kepler described how the planets move and how the orbits of the planets can be predicted. Kepler's laws proved that planets do not orbit the Sun in perfect circles. Instead, the shape of each orbit is an ellipse. In 1687, Newton published his *law of universal gravitation*. He used math to prove Kepler's laws. Astronomers could now confidently use the heliocentric model to accurately predict the positions of the planets and other objects in the solar system.

Johannes Kepler (right), an assistant to astronomer Tycho Brahe, built his theories on knowledge he gained from Brahe's work. Sir Isaac Newton then used Kepler's laws to formulate his own laws. Scientists can always learn from the work of others.

Stop and Think

1. Models often form the basis of a scientific theory. One thing that all scientific theories must do is make accurate predictions. Scientists will accept a theory until a better theory comes along. Why do you think it took so long for the heliocentric model to be accepted?

2. Why was the heliocentric model accepted? In what ways was the heliocentric model better than the geocentric model?

3. What role did accurate observations play in the acceptance of the heliocentric model?

4. How do you think scientists use Newton's law of universal gravitation when trying to predict whether two solar-system objects will collide?

What's the Point?

Ancient astronomers recognized that some objects in the sky moved against the fixed background of the stars. These objects were called planets. Ptolemy's geocentric model, with Earth at the center, was widely accepted until the 1500s because it could accurately predict positions of the planets. A heliocentric model, with the Sun at the center of the solar system, was not widely accepted until the 1600s. A heliocentric model with elliptical orbits allows astronomers to accurately predict the positions of planets.

Planets closer to the Sun than Earth (Mercury and Venus) always appear in the sky near the Sun's location. That is why Mercury and Venus are only visible within a few hours of sunrise or sunset. Planets farther from the Sun can rise and set at any time.

The planets generally move in a counterclockwise direction in the sky, from west to east. However, during retrograde motion the outer planets, such as Mars and Jupiter, appear to reverse direction and move clockwise (east to west) for periods of time.

3.5 Explore

Where in the Solar System Are Smaller Objects Found?

In *Learning Set 1,* you read about some of the other objects in the solar system. You learned about dwarf planets and smaller solar system objects such as asteroids, comets, and meteoroids. Now that you have developed a model of the sizes and distances of the planets in the solar system, you can use that model as a map to help you understand where the other solar-system objects are found. You must know where those solar system objects can be found to know if solar-system objects will collide.

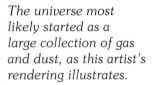

The universe most likely started as a large collection of gas and dust, as this artist's rendering illustrates.

Answering the question of where the other solar-system objects are located is easier if you understand how the solar system was formed. The solar system has not existed forever. The universe is about 14 billion years old, but the solar system formed less than 5 billion years ago.

Formation of the Solar System

Scientists have several theories about how the solar system formed. There are small differences in the theories, but they are all the same in many ways. All of the current theories say that the universe started as a large collection of gas and dust in space. This gas and dust was in a cloud much greater in size than the orbit of Neptune. The gas and dust started to spin and collapse in on itself. As parts of the cloud spun faster and faster around the center, and different pieces collided with each other, the cloud became a flattened disk with a bulge at the center. The center of the bulge became very hot, and as soon as it was hot enough for fusion to occur, the Sun was officially born.

According to current theories, most of the mass in the cloud collapsed inward to form the Sun. But the parts that remained outside the bulge in the disk continued to collide and combine with each other. Eventually, eight little balls formed within the disk, sweeping up everything in their path. These eight balls eventually became the eight planets.

According to scientists, the parts of the mass that did not become part of the Sun continued to collide and combine with one another. As in this illustration, the remaining eight balls became the eight planets in our solar system. Not to scale.

This theory of the solar system's formation accounts for two important facts about the way the planets orbit the Sun. The planets all travel in the same direction around the Sun, counterclockwise, as seen from above. The planets orbit in the same direction around the Sun because the original disk was spinning in that direction. Also, all of the planets lie within the same *orbital plane* because they all formed within the flattened disk of matter surrounding the new Sun. You can think of the orbital plane of the solar system as a tabletop. The planets all orbit the Sun as if they were marbles rolling on the tabletop. Most solar-system objects have orbits that are tilted a little bit. This means that part of the orbit is above the orbital plane and part is below the orbital plane. Some objects have orbits that are tilted much more, but these orbits most likely were the result of collisions or near misses.

Remember the story of the Moon's formation that you read about in *Learning Set 2*. In this scenario, the Moon came into being after Earth had already formed. Because a collision probably brought about the Moon's formation, the Moon does not quite lie in the orbital plane of the planets. In fact, the Moon's orbit is tilted 5° away from the orbital plane.

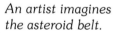
An artist imagines the asteroid belt.

According to these theories, even after the planets formed, there was still material left over from the formation of the solar system. The early history of the solar system was filled with collisions, the records of which still exist on the Moon and other objects in the solar system. Other bits of leftover material formed the other smaller objects in the solar system. For example, some rocky, iron-rich material collected in between the orbits of Mars and Jupiter. This collection of over one million rocky objects, each over a kilometer in diameter, is now called the *asteroid belt*.

Most asteroids are found in the asteroid belt. However, asteroids can be found throughout the solar system. Some of these other asteroids may have formed in the asteroid belt and then their orbits changed because they passed too close to Jupiter.

A million asteroids in one area seems like a lot. It may seem that collisions would occur all the time, at least within the asteroid belt. Have you ever watched a science fiction film with a "chase scene" through the asteroids? There are no doubt collisions among the asteroids as they tumble through space, which makes for exciting special effects. However, one thing to remember is that there is a lot of space in space! The area between the orbits of Mars and Jupiter is over two quintillion square kilometers (2,000,000,000,000,000,000 km^2) in size. If you assume that there are a million asteroids in the asteroid belt, and they all lie in the orbital plane, then there is only one asteroid per two trillion square kilometers (2,000,000,000,000 km^2) of the orbital plane. This means that in an area that is four times the area of Earth's surface, you would only find one rock about a kilometer in diameter.

Astronomers have investigated whether the asteroid belt could be debris left over from destruction of a planet between Mars and Jupiter. Scientists now think, though, that there is not enough debris in the asteroid belt to account for the destruction of such a planet.

Astronomers learn about the solar system through the use of telescopes in space, such as the Hubble, and on Earth. This telescope is part of NASA's Catalina Sky Survey in Arizona.

You know there is evidence on the Moon's surface of many impacts that occurred in the past. You also know that the Moon may have formed in a collision that occurred after the planets formed. Scientists think that the early solar system had much more debris than there is now. There may have been several periods of intense bombardment in the early solar system. During these periods, collisions would have occurred much more frequently than they do now. One way of thinking about this is that collisions are less likely now because most of the objects that would collide have already done so.

In science, a theory is the best explanation that scientists have at any given time. The best explanation is one that has lots of data to support it. To learn more about the formation of the solar system and about how objects in the solar system move, scientists collect data using telescopes and space probes. They also use computer models and simulations to help them test their theories. Scientists build computer models to match their theories, and they use them to simulate what happens in the universe over billions of years.

If a model is good, then the simulation will show solar-system objects moving in space the way we see them move today. The data astronomers collect from observing the sky and the data collected from computer simulations should match. If a theory about the formation of the solar system is accurate, the computer simulation should predict where astronomers would find other solar-system objects that have never been sighted before. When astronomers find solar-system objects they have not seen before, they gain evidence to support their theories. In science, the best theory is the one that explains available data and makes the best predictions.

Stop and Think

1. Describe the events that led to the formation of the solar system.

2. Why do the planets all move in the same direction around the Sun?

3. The asteroid belt contains over a million objects 1 kilometer or more in diameter and countless smaller objects. Why is it still correct to describe the asteroid belt as a relatively empty place?

Near-Earth Objects

Knowing about the formation of the solar system may give you some clues about where other smaller objects in the solar system might be found and how they move. Smaller objects that orbit around larger objects are called **satellites**. Many of the objects in the solar system lie in well-defined orbits that do not cross Earth's orbit, so they are unlikely to collide with Earth. Other objects are moons of other planets. These moons will never stray far from the planet they orbit. Gravity from the planet they orbit will keep them far from the orbits of other planets.

Some of the smaller solar-system objects, such as comets, have flattened elliptical orbits. When they are far from the Sun, beyond the orbit of Neptune, comets travel slowly. Some take thousands of years to orbit once around the Sun. But because their orbits are very elliptical, their path is more likely to cross the path of a planet, similar to the way the Shoemaker-Levy 9 comet crossed paths with Jupiter.

Another factor in determining whether an object will collide with a solar-system object is whether the object's orbit is *inclined*. Some dwarf planets, such as Pluto, have orbits that are inclined at a great angle from the orbital plane of the solar system. This means that they are much less likely to cross the path of another planet because they do not spend much time in the orbital plane.

> **satellite:** a smaller object that is in orbit around a larger object.
>
> **Near-Earth Objects (NEOs):** asteroids and comets that cross the orbit of Earth.

Any asteroids and comets that cross the orbit of Earth are tracked by the governments of the world. These objects are classified as **Near-Earth Objects (NEOs)**. Once an NEO is detected, it is reported and monitored. In the United States, NASA catalogs all NEOs that have the potential to be catastrophic if they collided with Earth. Scientists monitor the orbits of NEOs and investigate questions such as how many there are, their origins, and their threat to Earth.

Stop and Think

1. Does a space object have to have an Earth-crossing orbit in order to collide with Earth? Why or why not?

2. Do you think the number of objects listed as Near-Earth Objects is always increasing, or could the list become shorter?

Reflect

1. Look back to the kinds of objects listed on your *Solar System* page. Which of these objects do you think are most likely to have a collision with another solar-system object?

2. Which solar-system objects do you think are very unlikely to collide with Earth? Why?

3. Which solar-system objects do you think would be most likely to collide with Earth? Why?

Update the *Project Board*

You have read a little about the formation of the solar system and the location of small solar-system objects. Your *Project Board* may have questions like *Where did all of these solar-system objects come from?* and *How did the solar system form?* You can now start to answer these questions in the *What we are learning?* and *What is our evidence?* columns.

Your reading may have raised more questions. For example, you might wonder *Where do comets come from?* If there are still things you are unsure about, or things that, if answered, would increase your confidence about what you think you know, record them in the *What do we need to investigate?* column.

What's the Point?

The solar system formed from a cloud of gas and dust a little less than 5 billion years ago. The Sun formed in the middle, and the planets formed from the leftover gas and dust that had collected in a disk around the Sun. Material that did not go into the formation of planets made up the asteroids, comets, and other objects that travel around the solar system. Near-Earth Objects (NEOs) are those objects that cross Earth's orbit.

Learning Set 3

Back to the Big Question

How can you know if objects in space will collide?

In this *Learning Set,* in you learned a lot about the structure and motion of the solar system. Use what you have learned to update your *Solar System* page. You learned about the positions of objects in the solar system. You also learned about motions of objects in the solar system. You constructed several different models of the solar system. You can add the ideas you got from these explorations to your *Solar System* page.

Now that you have a better understanding of the solar system, it may be easier for you to understand what objects might collide in space. Use what you have learned in *Learning Set 3* to add to your *Big Question* page. After the next *Learning Set,* you will use the information on this page to construct your report.

At the beginning of this *Learning Set* you became an expert on the Sun or one of the planets in the solar system. You developed a description of what would happen if a 10-kilometer asteroid collided with your object. Your idea of what would happen might have changed as you proceeded through the rest of the *Learning Set.* A good way to prepare for your report on collisions is to revise this description based on what you just learned. You might also be able to add details to your description. For example, you can now describe what could cause the orbit of a 10-kilometer asteroid to change, leading to a collision with your object.

Conference

To complete your understanding of the solar system, and the ways scientists determine if two objects in space will collide, you need to find out more about what happened to the debris left after the formation of the solar system.

Each of the following terms relates to a part of the solar system other than the eight planets and the asteroid belt.

- Kuiper Belt

- Trans-Neptunian Objects

- Oort Cloud

- Centaur planets

Your group will be assigned one of these terms to study and explore. Using available resources, determine the characteristics and the origins of the objects described by your term. Determine if any of these objects have ever been classified as Near-Earth Objects. Then determine the likelihood that such an object will ever collide with other space objects. Use this information to prepare a presentation for the class.

Your presentation should include the size and location of your objects, how they were discovered, how long they take to orbit the Sun, whether a large planet could alter their orbit, and which other orbits cross theirs.

Communicate

Share Your Data

Listen to each group as they give their presentation. If different groups are covering the same material, see if the information gathered by each group is in agreement. Try to resolve any differences in the findings of the groups.

As you listen to each presentation, if you disagree with, or do not understand, a group's presentation, ask questions. Make sure you ask respectfully. Some good questions to ask include:

- What are the objects made of and how big are they?

- How were the objects discovered?

- How long do they take to orbit the Sun?

- Is it likely for the objects to have their orbits altered by Jupiter or another large planet?

- Which orbits of other space objects cross the orbit of their space object?

After listening to all of the presentations, add the most important findings to your *Big Question* page. Some of the information you heard may make it into your report on the likelihood of an object from space colliding with Earth.

Revise Your Explanation

In this *Learning Set,* you learned about the structure of the solar system beyond Earth, the Moon, and the Sun. Now it is time to use this knowledge to revise your claim and explanation from the end of *Learning Set 2.* Use what you have recorded on your *Solar System* and *Big Question* pages to help you revise your claim and explanation. Edit your old *Create Your Explanation* page to make a revised explanation, or use a new one. Remember that a good explanation has several parts to it.

- **your claim:** a statement of what you understand or a conclusion you have reached

- **your evidence:** data collected from investigations that support your claim

- **your science knowledge:** knowledge about how things work that supports your claim

- **your explanation:** a logical statement connecting your evidence and science knowledge to your claim in a way that can convince someone that your claim is valid. Good explanations tell what is happening that makes the claim valid.

Your claim will be your clearest, most accurate statement about how to determine whether space objects will collide. Your evidence comes from your models of the solar system and from the information you have gathered on planets and other objects in the solar system. Your science knowledge comes from your reading. Work with your group to develop the best explanation you can. It may be easier to express your explanation by attaching phrases to sketches than to simply use words. Feel free to combine sketches and words in your explanation.

Communicate

Share Your Explanation

Share your group's explanation with the rest of the class. As you are listening to the explanation of others, look for anything they have included in their claims and explanations that you might have left out. With the class, agree on a claim and an explanation.

Reflect

With your group, answer the following questions.

1. How trustworthy and complete do you think your explanation is?

2. What else do you need to investigate and learn about the solar system to improve your explanation of how scientists can know if two space objects will collide?

Update the *Project Board*

You have collected a lot of information about the objects that move in the solar system. This information is important for addressing the *Big Question* for this Unit, *How can you know if objects in space will collide?* You may want to add more to the *Project Board* about the objects you learned about in this *Back to the Big Question.* Remember that any information added to the *What are we learning?* column should be supported with evidence in the *What is our evidence?* column.

Add any new questions you have identified to the *What do we need to investigate?* column. Add questions you need answered about objects that are outside of the solar system to determine if objects in space can collide. Finally, add to the *What does this mean for the question?* column anything you now know about answering the *Big Question: How can you know if objects in space will collide?*

Learning Set 4

How Do Objects Outside Our Solar System Move Through Space?

Astronomers use Newton's laws of motion and gravity to predict accurately the motion of many solar-system objects. As soon as a new solar-system object is identified, its location and speed are measured from Earth at several points in its orbit. From this data, the entire orbit can be calculated. Once the orbit is known, astronomers can compare it to the known orbits of the planets and other solar-system objects to predict whether the newly identified object is on a collision course.

space probe: a remotely controlled spacecraft with data collection equipment used to gather data about objects in space.

However, accurately determining the orbits of objects in our solar system can be difficult. Because the images we see through telescopes are distorted by Earth's atmosphere, scientists also use other technologies to explore what is happening in space. They can launch a **space probe** from Earth that will send back photographs and other information. Scientists have also launched telescopes into space. A telescope in space can "see" dimmer objects and also provide sharper images than a telescope used on Earth.

An artist's version of the space probe, Voyager 1 in flight.

The photographs and other data collected by space probes and telescopes have helped scientists study stars and discover space objects and even whole solar systems outside of our solar system. This data have also allowed scientists to investigate the origin of the universe. All of this information has helped scientists develop a detailed picture of our place in the universe.

For example, in 1977, NASA launched two probes, *Voyager 1* and *Voyager 2* to study the outer planets. The probes took advantage of the outer planets being lined up for the first time in many years. *Voyager 2* was able to pass by all four outer planets on its tour of the solar system. Another tour like this will not be possible until 2157. The two probes transmitted exciting images and data of planets and moons seen close-up for the first time. Scientists learned much about the composition and orbits of the outer planets and their moons.

Even today, scientists are receiving signals from the two probes. In 2009, *Voyager 1* was 110 AU from the Sun. In the year 2015, scientists expect *Voyager 1* to become the first probe to leave the solar system. In 40,000 years it will pass close to another star.

So far in this Unit you have focused on objects in our solar system that could collide with one another. In this *Learning Set,* you will focus on objects outside of our solar system. You will explore the stars and other objects in the universe—where they are, how they move, and how we use technology to learn about them.

This composite image of Neptune on Triton's horizon was made from images taken by Voyager 2. Triton is the largest of Neptune's moons. Not to scale.

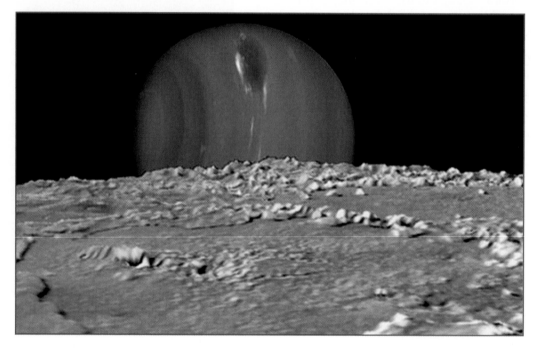

4.1 Understand the Question

Think About How Objects Outside Our Solar System Move Through Space

When you look at the night sky, you can see thousands of stars. They all appear as dazzling, twinkling points of light. Some stars are very bright, and some are so dim you can barely see them. Are the brighter stars closer, or are they giving off more light? And are the stars really fixed, or do they move through space? These are questions astronomers have been asking for hundreds of years.

It would seem that there is little that you can learn from gazing at a point of light and comparing it to other points of light. But astronomers have been able to study the light from stars in many ways. They also have learned much by studying Earth's closest star, the Sun. One thing they have learned through these studies is that Newton's laws of motion and gravity apply to the stars. In *Learning Set 2* and *Learning Set 3,* you read about how astronomers were able to infer the structure of the solar system from what they saw in the sky. Now you will learn how scientists have built up a three-dimensional moving model of the universe from what they see in the sky as well.

Get Started

Scientists use photographic images to study objects in the night sky. They make some assumptions about what types of objects would have produced the images. They also compare different objects within an image or different images of the same part of the sky taken at different times. You will practice using these same methods in two investigations.

Each group will be assigned one photograph. Study your image. Compare the different lights in the image. Notice how the lights are similar to or different from one another. Then work as a group to answer the questions.

Image #1

Image #2

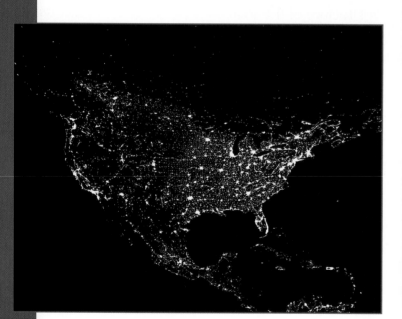

Image #3

1. Do you think all of the lights in your photograph are the same distance away from the camera, or are some of the lights closer and some farther? What evidence suggests the distance of each light from the camera?

2. Do you think all the lights would be the same brightness if they were viewed from a distance of 100 meters, or do you think some lights are brighter and some are not as bright? What evidence did you use to decide?

3. What do you think your image is? What evidence supports your conclusion? What additional information besides the image itself do you need to be sure about what it is?

4. What assumptions have you made about the objects that are producing the lights in your image?

Communicate

Share Your Conclusions

Each group should show its image to the class and share its answers to the four questions. As you listen to others, pay attention to the information each group was able to gather from its image. Try to determine if the group could have come to other conclusions based on the same information. Notice how much information from the image each group uses to draw its conclusions and how much knowledge they apply from other sources.

Reflect

1. In each image, how much of the information gathered was in the image itself, and how much was inferred from other sources of information?

2. What factors do you think determine the brightness of a star in the sky?

3. Do you think all stars are the same size? Why do you think some are brighter than others?

4. Do you think there might be stars that are moving toward our solar system? How do you think the light from a star would change if the star were getting closer to us?

ASTRONOMY

5. Think about all the prior knowledge you needed to analyze the images in the investigation. Then think about what knowledge you need to understand images of stars in the sky. What do you think you need to investigate to know more about the location and movement of space objects outside of our solar system?

6. What do you think you need to investigate to decide whether any of those space objects might enter our solar system and collide with solar-system objects?

Update the *Project Board*

In the *What do we think we know?* column, record what you know about stars and other space objects outside of our solar system. Also record knowledge you used to interpret the photographs. In the *What do we need to investigate?* column, record questions you have about stars and space objects outside of our solar system. Also record any ideas you have about investigations that will help you better understand the distances between stars and the motion of stars other than the Sun.

How can you know if objects in space will collide?				
What do we think we know?	What do we need to investigate?	What are we learning?	What is our evidence?	What does it mean for the challenge or question?

What's the Point?

From your class discussions, you have probably realized that even a simple photograph can be interpreted in more than one way. This suggests that if you want to draw conclusions from the data in a photograph, it would be a good idea to confirm your conclusions with additional information that is not in the photograph. Think about this in the next section as you explore brightness of stars and distances to the stars.

4.2 Explore

How Can You Know How Bright a Star Is and How Far Away It Is?

At the beginning of *Section 4.1,* you thought about a question astronomers have investigated for many years: *Are the brighter stars closer, or are they giving off more light?* You will now have the chance to explore factors that affect the brightness of stars. You will also find out how astronomers determine distances to the closest stars.

When you compare two lights in a photograph, as you did in the last section, the brightness of each light depends on at least two factors. One factor is how much light is given off by the light source. For example, a streetlight gives off more light than a 25-watt light bulb, so you would expect a streetlight to look brighter than a 25-watt light bulb.

Suppose, however, that you stand 1 meter from a 25-watt light bulb and 100 meters from a streetlight. Now the 25-watt light bulb will appear brighter than the streetlight. The distance to a light source is a second factor that affects the brightness of light that enters your eyes. The farther away you are from a light source, the less bright it will appear to your eyes.

The streetlight in the photograph on left looks very bright. How bright would it look from a block away? What about 10 blocks away? Or 100 blocks away?

ASTRONOMY

What Other Factor Affects How Bright an Object Appears?

Now you will work with a partner to discover another factor that affects how bright an object appears to be. You and your partner will record observations made in Steps 2–5, using a table like the one below.

	Left eye	Right eye
Appearance of each eye after five minutes in the dark		
Differences in what each eye sees after one eye is covered for one minute	Covered—	Uncovered—
Appearance of each eye at the end of the activity		

Materials

• watch or clock with second hand

Procedure

1. Work "in the dark" for five minutes, with the room lights off. If there are shades in the room, they will be pulled down to keep the room dark. During this time, you should not look at any bright sources of light, such as a computer screen. Follow instructions about what work do during these five minutes.

2. After the five minutes have passed, have your partner look at your eyes and record observations in the first row of your table. At the same time, you will observe your partner's eyes and record observations in his or her table.

3. Cover your left eye with your hand for one minute. Your teacher will turn on the ceiling lights and also keep track of the time. During this minute, look up at the ceiling lights of your classroom with your right eye (keeping your left eye covered).

4. After one minute has passed, look at one wall of the classroom, first with your left eye open and your right eye closed, and then with your right eye open and your left eye closed. Repeat this a few times and record what you see.

5. You and your partner should now look at each other's eyes and record observations in the last row of the table.

Stop and Think

1. How did the appearance of your eyes after the activity compare with their appearance before the activity?

2. How did looking at a bright light with one eye change your vision in that eye? Did you and your partner experience the same change in vision?

3. How do you think the change in the appearance of your eyes affected your vision?

In the investigation, you discovered that another factor that affects the brightness of light you see is the size of your eyes' **pupils**. You may have noticed that when you look at a friend's eyes in bright sunlight, the pupils of his or her eyes are small. In bright light, your eyes protect themselves by reducing the size of the pupils, which reduces the amount of light that enters your eyes. In darkness, your pupils grow larger to allow more light into your eyes. This helps you to see in the dark.

pupil: the circular opening in the center of the eye that controls the amount of light that enters the eye.

If you step outside on a clear night, at first you do not see many stars. Your pupils are still small from seeing bright indoor lights. After you have been outside for several minutes, your eyes are better adjusted to the darkness. Your pupils are much larger now. If you are far from city lights, now you can see thousands of stars. When your pupils are larger, they allow more light to enter your eyes. You can see a greater number of stars that are dim. These dim stars were there before your eyes adjusted to the dark, and they were just as bright. Your eyes could not detect the dim stars because too little light entered your eyes.

You may know that owls and other animals that see well in the dark benefit from having large eyes. The easiest way for humans to see better in the dark is to use binoculars. You may think binoculars only help you to see small details, but they also help you see objects that are too dim to see with the unaided eye. The lenses in binoculars are much larger than your pupils, so these "bigger eyes" collect more light than your eyes collect.

Suppose you look at one area of the sky, first with the binoculars and then without them. You can see many more stars with binoculars, more than a hundred thousand stars if you are far from city lights. This may make you wonder how many stars you could see if you were able to see every star in the universe.

When you use binoculars, you notice that some stars appear a lot brighter than others. Astronomers use a number called **apparent magnitude** to compare the brightness of stars in the night sky. The smaller the number, the brighter the star appears. With binoculars, you can see stars with an apparent magnitude of about 9 or less. Using only your unaided eyes, in good conditions you can see stars with an apparent magnitude of about 6 or less. The brightest stars have negative apparent magnitudes. The brightest star in the night sky, Sirius, has an apparent magnitude of about –1.5. The Sun is much brighter, with an apparent magnitude of –27.

Astronomers use a number called **absolute magnitude** to describe how bright a star would be if it were viewed from a standard distance, which happens to be about 2 million astronomical units. For example, the Sun has an absolute magnitude of 4.8, while Sirius has an absolute magnitude of 1.4. So, Sirius would be much brighter than the Sun if the two stars were viewed from the same distance.

Compare Distances Using Parallax

You might wonder how scientists know how far away from Earth a star is. After all, a star could be bright because it is close to our solar system, or it could be bright because it gives off a lot of light. Scientists use a measurement called **parallax** to determine distances to stars. Parallax is the observable change in an object's apparent position when observed from two locations that are the same distance from the object. In the next investigation, you will use parallax to compare distances in your classroom or in a hallway near your classroom. This exploration will help you understand what parallax means and how it can be used to determine how far a star is from Earth.

Your teacher has set up observation areas at four stations. Two are set up for Investigation 1, and two are set up for Investigation 2. Your group will be visiting one of the stations and doing one of the investigations. In each investigation, you will make sketches of your observations of three different objects against a distant background. Everyone will draw two sketches of what they observe. To carry out the investigation correctly, you will need to read the entire procedure for your investigation before you begin. You will record your sketches on a *Parallax View* page.

apparent magnitude: the brightness of a star relative to other stars as seen from Earth.

absolute magnitude: the brightness a star would be relative to other stars if all were viewed from the same distance (about 2 million astronomical units).

parallax: the observable change in an object's apparent position relative to a distant background when observed from two locations that are the same distance from the object.

Materials

- ruler
- objects A, B, and C placed on desks
- masking tape for marking observation X's
- *Parallax View* pages

Investigation 1: Procedure

Take turns following this procedure. Each person in your group should have a turn.

1. On the observation desk there will be one X marked by masking tape. Kneel on the floor and rest your chin on the X.

2. Close your left eye, or hold your left hand over your left eye. With your right eye, study objects A, B, and C on the tables in front of you.

3. Still looking with your right eye only, sketch the three objects in the *Sketch 1* box on your *Parallax View* page. Use most of the full width of the drawing area to make your sketch.

4. Still looking with your right eye only, and with your chin in the same position, study the far wall of the room. Add background details to your sketch to show which part of the background is behind each object.

5. Copy your sketch of the background from *Sketch 1* onto *Sketch 2* on your *Parallax View* page. Do not include objects A, B, or C. Draw the background to the same scale as in *Sketch 1.*

6. Now, put your chin back in exactly the same position as it was when you made your observations for *Sketch 1.* This time, open your left eye, and close your right eye. Sketch the three objects as seen by your left eye in the *Sketch 2* box on your *Parallax View* page. Make sure you show correctly which part of the background is behind each object.

Investigation 2: Procedure

Take turns following this procedure. Each person in your group should have a turn.

1. On the observation desk there will be two X's marked by masking tape. The centers of the X's are 50 cm apart. Kneel on the floor and rest your chin on the left X.

Parallax View 4.2.1

Name:_____ Date:_____
Group:_____

Distance between observation points: _____

Sketch 1

Sketch 2

Object	Description	Parallax—distance object shifted on background (in mm)	Actual distance from X to object (in mm)
A			
B			
C			
D			

Comparison between parallax and actual measurements: _____

2. You will make all of your observations with one eye closed and one eye open. Choose your left or your right eye, whichever you are more comfortable using. Close your other eye, or hold your hand over your other eye. Looking with one eye, study objects A, B, and C on the tables in front of you.

3. Still looking with the same eye, sketch the three objects in the *Sketch 1* box on your *Parallax View* page. Use most of the full width of the drawing area to make your sketch.

4. Still looking with one eye only and with your chin in the same position, study the far wall of the room. Add background details to your sketch to show which part of the background is behind each object.

5. Copy your sketch of the background from *Sketch 1* onto *Sketch 2* on your *Parallax View* page. Do not include objects A, B, or C. Draw the background to the same scale as in *Sketch 1*.

6. Move your chin to the X on the right side of the observation desk. Using the same eye that you chose in Step 2 (covering or closing the other eye), sketch the three objects in the *Sketch 2* box on your *Parallax View* page. Make sure to correctly show which part of the background is behind each object.

Analyze Your Data

Begin by looking at the differences in your two sketches. You should see that, although you were the same distance from the objects when you made both sketches, the objects are sketched in different places relative to the background. This is parallax. To use this method to compare distances to objects, scientists usually measure parallax on photographs. You will measure parallax on your sketch.

1. The first thing you need to record is the actual distance between your observation places. For those who did Investigation 2, the distance was 50 cm. For those who did Investigation 1, the distance was the distance between your two eyes. You may measure that distance, or you can use a distance of 5 cm, the average distance between people's eyes. Record the distance between your two observation points at the top of your *Parallax View* page.

2. Measure the parallax on your sketches. Using a ruler, measure the distance each object appeared to shift on your sketches. Measure in millimeters. Record the parallax in the middle column of the chart on your *Parallax View* page.

3. Measure the actual distances to objects A, B, and C in millimeters. Record your measurements in the last column of the chart on your *Parallax View* page.

4. Compare your parallax measurements to the actual distance to the objects. Record how the two measurements compare at the bottom of your *Parallax View* page.

Communicate

Share Your Results

Your teacher will make two tables, one table to collect all of the parallax measurements that the class made for Investigation 1 and one table for all of the parallax measurements for Investigation 2. When your group takes its turn sharing data, report which investigation your group carried out, then report the parallax measurements your group made for objects A, B, and C. Describe how you think parallax relates to the distance of an object.

After all of the data have been collected, examine the charts together. Discuss the results. Did any of the results surprise you? Discuss how accurately your parallax measurements could be used to compare actual distances to the objects. Then discuss how the procedure you followed might be used by astronomers to measure the distances to stars in the sky. What do you think are the difficulties in taking such measurements?

Stop and Think

1. Which objects appear to have greater parallax when you shift observation points, objects closer to you or objects farther away? Why?

2. Which groups observed a greater parallax for each object, students performing Investigation 1 or students performing Investigation 2? Why?

3. Which groups had difficulty in measuring parallax for Object C, those who did Investigation 1 or those who did Investigation 2? Why?

Reflect

Scientists can only use parallax to find the distances to nearby stars. However, the parallax shift is very small, so it is difficult to measure.

1. What could you do to try to make the parallax easier to measure?

2. On Earth, what is the greatest distance apart that two observation points could be?

3. Think about Earth's orbit around the Sun. How do you think scientists might use two different observation points on Earth's orbit to calculate the distances to nearby stars? What positions in an orbit are farthest from each other? What is the advantage of using observation points that are this far apart?

Measuring Parallax of Stars

Exploring parallax of objects in your classroom is a bit easier than measuring parallax of stars. In the classroom, you only used parallax to compare distances. You could have checked your comparisons using a tape measure for the actual distances. Scientists, of course, cannot use a tape measure to find the actual distance to a star, but they can use parallax and geometry to calculate actual distances.

In your investigation, you learned that if you increase the distance between your observation points, the parallax you observe increases. To measure parallax to the stars, astronomers observe a star at one time of the year and then observe it again six months later. If the star is much closer than the other stars in the photograph, then the parallax shows up as a shift in the position of the star. In fact, the parallax is so small that it can only be measured using a telescope.

In *Learning Set 2,* you discovered that the angle from the horizon to directly overhead is 90°, and you used degrees to measure the size of the Moon. Instead of measuring parallax as a distance, as you did, astronomers measure parallax in fractions of a degree. They draw imaginary lines from each of the observation points to the star, and then they measure the angle the lines form. Then they use geometry to calculate the actual distance from Earth to the star.

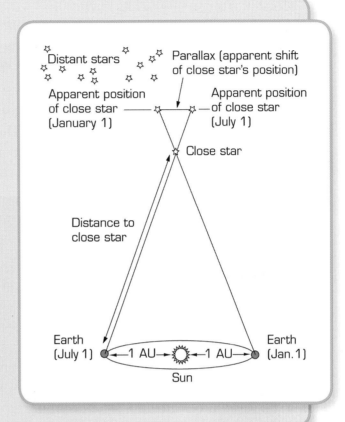

Reflect

1. Why do you think astronomers want to know the distances to stars?

2. What more would you need to know to decide whether stars are inside our solar system?

What's the Point?

Several factors affect the brightness of stars. The more light a star gives off, the brighter it will appear. However, the farther you are from a star, the dimmer it will appear to be. The brightness of a star, as viewed from Earth, is given by its apparent magnitude. Scientists describe the amount of light a star gives off by stating its absolute magnitude. This is the magnitude the star would have if it were about 2 million AU from Earth. Stars that are bright enough to be seen without binoculars are either very close, very bright, or both.

Parallax is the apparent shift in an object's position when viewed from two observation points that are equal distances from the object. As the distance to an object increases, the parallax decreases. The parallax that you can observe can be increased by observing from two observation points with a greater separation.

Parallax is measurable if you make observations that are six months apart, when Earth is at opposite ends of its orbit. The distance between the observation points, 2 AU, is great enough to make it possible to use a telescope to observe parallax for the closest stars.

The Spitzer telescope is orbiting the Sun, away from Earth. Its images can be compared to Earth-based images, allowing scientists to compare images taken at the same time from two different points in space.

4.3 Read

The Milky Way

One goal of astronomy is to make a map that shows the characteristics and locations in space of the stars in Earth's neighborhood, not just how they appear in the sky. To determine if a star could collide with another space object, you must understand how stars are organized.

In *Learning Set 3,* you read that the planets and other objects in our solar system formed from a large cloud of gas and dust and are organized into a system. Stars are also organized into systems. These systems are called galaxies. A **galaxy** is a system of stars, gas, and dust that is held together by the force of gravity. Earth and the Sun are part of the Milky Way galaxy. All of the stars you see in the sky are in the Milky Way galaxy. You already know that you can see thousands of stars in the sky with your unaided eye if you are far from city lights. When you use binoculars, as you know, that number jumps to hundreds of thousands of stars. But that is just a small fraction of the number of stars in the galaxy. The Milky Way galaxy contains hundreds of billions of stars!

galaxy: a system of stars, gas, and dust held together by gravity.

How Far Away Are the Stars in Our Galaxy?

To understand how our Sun and other stars are organized in the galaxy, astronomers have constructed maps and models of the Milky Way. To produce these maps, they needed to determine how far away the stars are. In the last section, you learned about the parallax method, which can be used to determine the distance to closer stars, including Alpha Centauri. To estimate the distance to other stars, astronomers assume that stars of the same type have the same brightness. Brighter stars of the same type are closer than dimmer stars of the same type. (You will learn more about types of stars in *Section 4.5.*)

In *Learning Set 3,* you read about the astronomical unit, or AU. The AU is equal to the average distance from Earth to the Sun. It is much easier to talk about distances in the solar system in AUs than in kilometers. However, the closest star system to Earth, Alpha Centauri, is about 280,000 AU from Earth. To make it easier to compare distances to stars, astronomers needed a new unit, so they could use smaller, easier-to-grasp numbers. The unit they use most often is called a **light year**.

A light year is the distance light can travel in one year. The speed of light is about 300,000 km/s. Light from the Sun reaches Earth in just over 8 minutes. In a year, light travels 9,460,000,000,000 km, so one light year is about 9.5 trillion kilometers. A light year is a unit that is convenient for measuring distances in the Milky Way galaxy. Alpha Centauri is about 4.4 light-years from Earth.

Looking at Samples of Stars in Our Galaxy

To build an accurate map of the Milky Way, astronomers would have to determine the characteristics and positions of over 200 billion stars. That task would be very difficult, but astronomers can determine the basic shape of the Milky Way by studying a **sample**, or subset, of stars in the sky. To accurately describe stars in the Milky Way galaxy astronomers need to observe sample stars that are **representative** of the rest of the stars in the galaxy. A subset is representative of a whole set if it has the same characteristics as the whole set.

light year: a unit of distance equal to the distance light travels in a year, about 9,460,000, 000,000 km.

sample: a subset of a set for which data are collected.

representative: describing a subset that has characteristics that closely match the characteristics of the whole set.

biased sample: a sample that does not accurately represent the group from which it was drawn.

With so many stars in the sky, it would be easy to choose a **biased sample** of stars to examine. A biased sample is a subset of a set that has characteristics that are very different than those of the full set. Examining a biased sample would tell you only about that sample. You could not learn about the whole set of stars if you studied a sample that were all bright, all dim, all close to Earth, or all far away.

These three stars of the Alpha Centauri system (left) are the closest to the Sun.

25 Brightest Stars as Seen from Earth			25 Closest Stars to Earth	
Star	**Absolute Magnitude**		**Star**	**Absolute Magnitude**
Deneb	–8.7		Sirius A	1.5
Rigel	–6.7		Procyon A	2.7
Canopus	–5.6		Alpha Centauri A	4.4
Antares	–5.4		Alpha Centauri B	5.7
Hadar	–5.4		Epsilon Eridani	6.2
Shaula	–5.1		61 Cygnus A	7.5
Betelgeuse	–5.0		61 Cygnus B	8.3
Acrux	–4.2		Lacaille 9352	9.8
Adhara	–4.1		GX Andromedae	10.3
Mimosa	–3.9		Lalande 21185	10.4
Spica	–3.6		Sigma 2398 A	11.2
Achernar	–2.8		Sirius B	11.3
Aldebaran	–0.6		Sigma 2398 B	12.0
Regulus	–0.5		Procyon B	13.0
Capella	–0.5		Ross 154	13.1
Arcturus	–0.3		Barnard's Star	13.2
Vega	0.6		Ross 128	13.5
Castor	0.6		Ross 248	14.8
Pollux	1.1		BL Ceti	15.4
Sirius A	1.4		Proxima Centauri	15.5
Fomalhaut	1.7		EZ Aquarii A	15.6
Altair	2.2		EZ Aquarii B	15.6
Procyon A	2.7		UV Ceti	15.9
Alpha Centauri A	4.4		EZ Aquarii C	16.3
Alpha Centauri B	5.7		Wolf 359	16.6

NOTE: Table does not include the Sun.

Stop and Think

The table on the previous page shows the absolute magnitude of each star, which is a measure of how much light each star gives off. The first column shows the 25 brightest stars you see in the night sky (based on apparent magnitude). The second column shows the 25 closest stars in the night sky. You can see that the characteristics of stars in the two lists are very different.

1. According to the sample of the 25 brightest stars as seen from Earth, are most stars very bright in absolute magnitude or very dim? How is this sample of the visible stars in the night sky biased?

2. According to the sample of the 25 stars closest to Earth, are most stars very bright in absolute magnitude or very dim? How is this sample of stars biased?

3. Four stars, Alpha Centauri A, Alpha Centauri B, Procyon A, and Sirius A are on both lists. Why do you think these stars are dimmer in absolute magnitude than most of the other stars on the 25 brightest stars list?

4. Which list do you think more accurately represents the absolute brightness of stars in the night sky? Support your answer using the data.

The Structure of the Milky Way

By choosing a representative sample of stars in the sky, astronomers have been able to make a map of the galaxy. The image on the facing page is a photograph of the Milky Way galaxy. The galaxy has a bright bulge in the center and several spiral arms. The Milky Way is about 100,000 light-years across and contains between 200 billion and 400 billion stars. The Sun is located in one spiral arm about 30,000 light-years from the center. The spiral arms all lie in a disk shape that is relatively thin, about 1,000 light-years deep. The bright center of the galaxy bulges out from the disk. There are many more stars close to the center of the galaxy than in the spiral arms.

On Earth, because we are inside the galaxy, we must infer the shape of the Milky Way by mapping the stars we see in three dimensions. Imagine looking from the location of the Sun in the first image. You see stars in every direction, but those stars are relatively close to us within the same spiral arm of the galaxy. Most of the stars are in the disk of the Milky Way galaxy, which appears as a faint band of light that stretches in a giant circle across the sky. You see a thicker, brighter band of stars when you look toward the center of the galaxy in the direction of the constellation Sagittarius. In the opposite direction, you see the band of stars continue, but it is much fainter because you are looking away from the galactic center. That is the view of the Milky Way galaxy that you have from Earth.

Until the invention of the telescope, observers could not tell that the band of light was made up of billions of stars. They could only tell it was a white band of light, which is what led to the name Milky Way.

Reflect

1. Compare the image of the galaxy to the solar system. How is the organization of the galaxy similar to that of the solar system, and how is it different? From the similarities, what can you infer about the center of the galaxy?

2. Using what you know about motions in the solar system, describe how you think the stars in the Milky Way move relative to each other.

What's the Point?

The Milky Way galaxy contains over 200 billion stars. Scientists have determined the basic shape of the galaxy by choosing a representative sample of the stars that are visible from Earth. The galaxy is disk-shaped with spiral arms in the disk and a central bulge. It is about 100,000 light-years in diameter, and the Sun is about 30,000 light-years from the center. A light year is a unit of distance equal to the distance that light can travel in one year.

The Milky Way galaxy, pictured above, resembles a giant pinwheel with swirling arms.

4.4 Explore

How Do Stars Move in the Milky Way Galaxy?

The stars are so far away that the fastest rocket ever built would take over 100,000 years to get to the nearest star beyond the Sun. Although scientists cannot send probes to study other stars, they can observe and measure the light that stars emit.

The Milky Way galaxy looks like a giant pinwheel, with a bright cluster at the center and several swirling arms. This pinwheel is not stationary. The stars within it are constantly in motion. In this section, you will investigate the relationships among the different parts of the Milky Way.

Demonstration

When you make chocolate milk, first you pour a large glass of milk, then you add the chocolate syrup. When you swirl around the milk with your spoon, you see a pattern of swirls on the surface of the milk. These swirls look a little like the spiral pattern in the Milky Way galaxy. You will now observe another demonstration that shows a pattern swirling about a center.

This photograph of the Milky Way was made by leaving the camera lens open for a long time. It shows some stars too dim to see with the unaided eye.

Project-Based Inquiry Science

is shorter, the pitch is higher. When the wavelength is longer, the pitch is lower. The faster a vehicle is moving, the greater the change in the pitch of the siren.

The same thing happens with light waves. Because stars are moving at great speeds toward and away from Earth, the dark line for hydrogen shifts from one area of the spectrum to another. The following demonstration will help you understand how this works.

Demonstration

Observe (Listen)

Your teacher will play three sound recordings. The first recording will be a whistle on a train that is not moving. In the second recording, you will hear the sound of a train whistle coming toward you. In the third recording, you will hear the sound of a train whistle moving away from you. You will get to hear each recording twice. Just listen the first time. After the second time, record your observations in a table like the one below. Then work together with your group to answer the questions.

	Description of train whistle
Train not moving	
Train moving toward you	
Train moving away from you	

Stop and Think

1. How is the sound of a train whistle that is not moving different from the sound of a train whistle that is moving toward you?

2. How is the sound of a train whistle that is not moving different from the sound of a train whistle that is moving away from you?

3. How do you think you could you use sound to determine if a train that is far away is moving toward you or away from you?

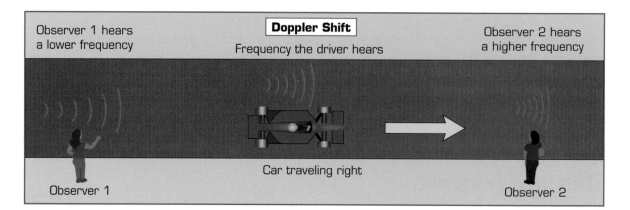

Doppler Shift

Observer 1 hears a lower frequency

Frequency the driver hears

Observer 2 hears a higher frequency

Car traveling right

Observer 1

Observer 2

blueshift: a shift in light toward the blue end of a spectrum, which occurs when the source of light is moving toward the observer.

redshift: a shift in light toward the red end of a spectrum, which occurs when the source of light is moving away from the observer.

Astronomers use Doppler shifts to tell whether stars are moving away from Earth or toward Earth. If the dark lines in a spectrum are shifted toward the blue end of the spectrum, where the wavelength is shorter, then the spectrum has a **blueshift**. A blueshift means the star is moving toward Earth. If the dark lines in the spectrum are shifted toward the red end of the spectrum, where the wavelength is longer, the spectrum has a **redshift**. A redshift means the star is moving away from Earth.

Astronomers also use Doppler shifts to tell how fast stars are moving toward or away from the observer. Astronomers can measure how fast stars move sideways with respect to Earth by measuring their position against the background stars over time. Together, the distances of stars and the motions of stars have been used to build up a map of the Milky Way galaxy.

Motion of Stars in the Galaxy

The Milky Way galaxy is in the shape of a disc that is about 100,000 light-years in diameter and 1000 light-years thick. The Milky Way galaxy has about 200 billion stars. This means that on average each star is in the middle of a cube more than 3 light-years on a side without any other stars in the cube. The Sun is a good example, as the nearest star to the Sun is about 4.2 light-years away.

The number of stars per unit volume (density of stars) in the central bulge of the Milky Way is much greater than the number of stars per unit volume (density of stars) on the edges. That means stars near the central bulge are closer to one another than stars near the Milky Way's edges. But the distances among stars are still vast. Like the solar system, the motion of the stars around the center of the galaxy is highly organized.

Most stars move in the same direction around the center of the galaxy in a nearly circular orbit. These orbits take a very long time to complete. The Sun's orbit takes about 225 million years to complete. In fact, the Sun has orbited the galaxy only about 20 times during its lifetime. In comparison, Earth has orbited the Sun nearly 4.6 billion times.

Despite the length of time it takes to complete an orbit, the Sun still travels very quickly in its orbit. The Sun is about 30,000 light-years from the center of the Milky Way, and it travels about 100,000 light-years to complete one full orbit. Its average speed in its orbit is about 250 km/h. In *Learning Set 3,* you learned that Earth travels at a speed of about 30 km/h around the Sun. The entire solar system travels with the Sun as it orbits the galactic center, so Earth actually moves much faster around the center of the galaxy than it does around the Sun.

This image, taken by the Spitzer telescope, shows three streams arcing over the Milky Way galaxy. These streams are the remains of ancient star clusters and dwarf galaxies that regroup and form new orbits.

Stop and Think

1. Suppose the Sun were closer to the center of the Milky Way galaxy. Do you think the Sun would be moving faster or more slowly than it does now in its orbit about the center of the galaxy? Why?

2. Earths orbits around the Sun while the Sun orbits around the center of our galaxy. A friend says this is like the Moon orbiting Earth as Earth orbits around the Sun. In what ways is that a good comparison? In what ways might the comparison be misleading?

3. Where in the Milky Way galaxy do you think collisions among stars are more likely—close to the center of the galaxy or near the edge? Why?

Reflect

In the last two sections, you learned about the structure and motions of the Milky Way galaxy.

1. How are the structures of our solar system and the Milky Way galaxy similar? How are they different?

2. How are the motions of our solar system and the Milky Way galaxy similar? How are the motions of these two systems different?

Update the *Project Board*

Add what you now know about stars and the milky way galaxy to the *What are we learning?* column of the *Project Board.* Be sure to support your ideas with evidence in the *What is our evidence?* column.

What's the Point?

Astronomers determine the motions of stars by observing their movement against a fixed background and by measuring the Doppler shift of the light they emit. The movement of most stars within the Milky Way galaxy is in the same direction, rotating about the center in nearly circular orbits.

4.5 Read

What Does a Star's Light Reveal About a Star?

So far, you have read about how astronomers figure out the distance to a star and how they determine what the motion of a star is. You may wonder what the different types of stars are, how bright each type is, and if any of these objects could collide with other space objects.

Looking up at the sky from your home, you can tell that stars are points of light and that some are brighter than others. If you look up at the sky on a clear night, far from city lights, you may notice that stars have different colors. Astronomers can take images of stars from satellites above Earth's atmosphere, which gives the clearest possible view of the stars. In this type of image, shown here, it is easy to see that the universe is filled with a wide variety of stars of many different colors.

Types of Stars

Annie Jump Cannon, a scientist at the Harvard College Observatory, began working on a catalog of stars in 1896. She had a strong background in math, physics, and astronomy. She worked at Harvard College for more than 40 years, classifying over 250,000 stars during her time there. She also developed the classification scheme for stars that astronomers still use. Cannon classified stars based on the surface

This image of the sky from space was taken by the Hubble Telescope.

One of the earliest astrophysicists, Annie Jump Cannon earned many honors for her groundbreaking work classifying stars. She credited her abilities to concentrate and record different stars partly on her lifelong hearing impairment.

temperature of each star. Astronomers determine the temperature of a star by looking at the star's spectrum. Cannon labeled the categories from hottest to coldest using these letters: O, B, A, F, G, K, and M. The Sun, for example, is a G-type star.

Stars are classified into one of several lettered types and given a number based on their color within that type.

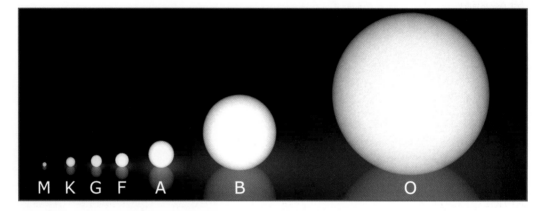

M K G F A B O

Around 1910, two astronomers, Einar Hertzsprung and Henry Norris Russell, independently studied Annie Jump Cannon's data. They both discovered a relationship between the brightness of stars and the surface temperature of stars. This relationship allowed astronomers to classify stars further.

Hertzsprung and Russell made a diagram to illustrate this relationship. It is known as the Hertzsprung-Russell diagram. On the Hertzsprung-Russell diagram, shown on the next page, the brightness of the stars is shown on the vertical axis, going from dimmer to brighter. The surface temperature is along the horizontal axis, going from hotter to cooler.

main sequence star: a typical star, usually with a diameter between one-eighth and 10 times the Sun's diameter.

giant star: a star that is larger than a main sequence star of the same color.

When the stars are plotted on the Hertzsprung-Russell diagram, most stars fall along a diagonal band. The stars in that band are known as main sequence stars because they are in what is called the main sequence. It is called the main sequence because most stars in it follow a relationship among brightness, temperature, and size. Blue stars are very hot and bright. The blue stars are also large. They may be more than 10 times the diameter of the Sun and tens of thousands of time brighter. Red stars are cool and dim. The red stars are also small. They are about an eighth the size of the Sun and hundred times dimmer than the Sun.

Giant stars are stars that are larger than the stars on the main sequence. These stars can have diameters 100 times greater than the Sun's diameter. If the Sun were replaced by such a giant star, Earth would orbit the star just about at the star's surface. **Supergiant** stars are the largest and brightest stars. The largest star known today has a diameter more than 2000 times the diameter of the Sun. If the Sun were replaced by this star, the star would extend all the way out to the orbit of Saturn. Supergiants can be millions of times brighter than the Sun.

On the lower left side of the diagram, white dwarfs are some of the dimmest stars in the universe. **White dwarfs** have a similar mass to that of the Sun, but the mass is packed into an area about the size of Earth. White dwarfs are thousands of times dimmer than the Sun.

Most stars in the sky seem to come in systems of two or more stars called *binary stars,* so the Sun is unusual in that it is a single star. Many stars in the sky are also variable stars because they vary in brightness in a periodic cycle. The Sun's brightness is very steady. That is why conditions on Earth do not change wildly. Scientists think that planets suitable for life are more likely to be found orbiting single stars that are stable like the Sun.

supergiant star: a star that is hundreds or thousands of times larger than a main sequence star of the same color.

white dwarf: a star about the same size as Earth, with about the same mass as the Sun.

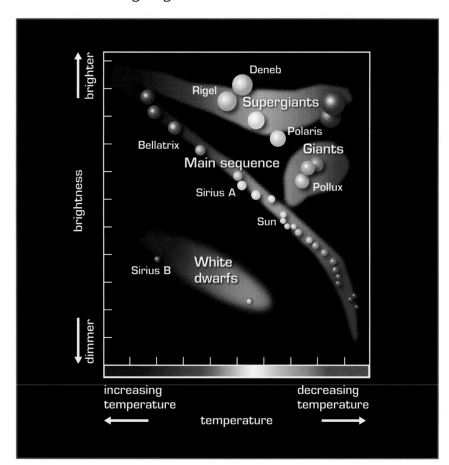

The Hertzsprung-Russell classification system of stars.

Radio Astronomy

Astronomers use more than just visible light to observe the universe. Often, clouds of gas and dust block our view of stars. For example, there is so much material in the way that we cannot see the center of the Milky Way galaxy using visible light. However, scientists can observe forms of *electromagnetic radiation* other than visible light, such as radio waves, infrared rays, and ultraviolet light.

Jocelyn Bell Burnell and Antony Hewish accidentally discovered the extraordinary celestial objects know as pulsars in 1967. While searching for an already known type of object that emits mostly radio waves, they found an object like nothing anyone had ever noticed before. This object emitted a radio pulse every 1.3 seconds. They originally called it LGM-1, with LGM standing for "little green men," because they were jokingly wondering if they had detected life outside the solar system.

In the next year it was proven that LGM-1 was a type of star now known as a *neutron star.* The star was emitting radio waves in a narrow jet while it was spinning. The jet is pointed at Earth every 1.3 seconds as the star spins around and around.

Astronomers are able to coordinate observations of radio waves in ways that are not yet possible with visible light. They can combine observations of the same object from radio telescopes all around Earth and even in space. This allows astronomers to construct a radio antenna that is in effect larger than the size of Earth. These *radio-telescope arrays* produce very sharp images of objects that emit radio waves.

This radio telescope, part of the NASA Deep Space Network in Canberra, Australia, is a radio antenna that detects radio signals from space.

The Death of Stars

Earlier in this *Learning Set,* you discovered that stars travel in predictable paths around the center of the Milky Way galaxy, so they are not likely to collide with any of the planets or with objects within our solar system. However, a star does pose a danger when it uses up the hydrogen fuel in its core.

You read in *Section 4.2* about the fusion reactions that take place in the core of the Sun. The energy that is produced in fusion prevents a star's mass from simply collapsing in on itself. Like the Sun, main sequence stars use hydrogen fusion to produce helium. However, eventually the star runs out of hydrogen in its core. What happens next depends on how much mass the star has.

Because fusion is what keeps a star from collapsing in on itself, once fusion stops the core of a star starts to collapse. As the atoms are squeezed together, the core becomes hotter and hotter.

For stars much smaller than the Sun, the core will never get hot enough for fusion of elements other than hydrogen. The star collapses until it becomes a white dwarf, and then it eventually cools off. (You will learn, however, that sometimes a white dwarf can behave in a spectacular way.)

A white dwarf, pictured as a large white mass in this artist's illustration, is a dying star. The other, ringed star is extremely dense and is attracting matter from the white dwarf through its force of gravity.

Stars with about the same mass as the Sun generate more heat in their cores when the core collapses than do the smaller stars. The outer part of the star expands, and the star becomes a red giant. The core heats up enough so that fusion of helium occurs. However, eventually even the helium runs out, and the star loses its ability to produce energy from fusion. The core collapses into a white dwarf. The outer layers drift away, sometimes forming a glowing ring of gas around a star. This is what will happen to the Sun. It will expand until it becomes a red giant and then collapse, becoming a white dwarf—but not until about five billion years from now.

supernova: an explosion of a white dwarf or a star several times the mass of the Sun.

neutron star: a supernova remnant with more mass than the Sun packed into a sphere about 20 kilometers in diameter.

black hole: a body with mass so concentrated that light cannot escape its gravitational pull.

Stars that are much more massive than the Sun go through several cycles of collapsing. After each collapse, heavier and heavier elements are used as fuel for fusion, until iron is produced. Fusion that produces elements heavier than iron does not occur. Heavy elements that cannot undergo fusion build up in the core. The core collapses and a spectacular explosion called a **supernova** takes place.

The core of the star that remains after a supernova is so compact that it has more mass than the Sun in a sphere that is about 20 kilometers across. This is called a **neutron star**. A neutron star is so dense that a cube one millimeter on a side from the middle of the star would weigh about 1000 kilograms (a little more than a ton).

Neutron stars cannot exist beyond a certain size, about twice the mass of the Sun. If the core of the star that remains after a supernova has more mass than this, a **black hole** is formed. A black hole is an object so dense that light cannot escape from it. Black holes cannot be seen directly because no light ever leaves a black hole to reach our eyes. However, their existence can be inferred from their strong gravitational pull.

Anything that comes too close to a black hole will be caught by the pull of its gravity, with no chance of escape. You can think of the black hole as mass concentrated at a single point. The more mass there is in a black hole, the stronger its gravitational pull. The largest black holes have the mass of millions of stars and sit at the centers of galaxies. These black holes can pull objects in from much farther away than is possible for a black hole that has the mass of a single star.

Stellar Explosions

You have learned that stars much larger than the Sun end in a massive explosion called a supernova. You may wonder how such explosions affect the area around a star. In 1054 C.E., people around the world noted what the Chinese astronomers called a "guest object" in the sky. For about three weeks, this object was bright enough to be seen during the day, becoming the third brightest object in the sky after the Sun and the Moon. After a couple of years, this object faded from the night sky and could no longer be seen.

The Crab Nebula is the remnant of a supernova seen 1000 years ago.

These ancient observers saw a supernova that took place over 7000 light-years from Earth. The supernova was the result of a star running out of fuel for fusion. The star exploded to form a neutron star. This star was too far away to have any effect on Earth besides briefly adding a new object to the night sky. At this location in the sky, astronomers now see the Crab Nebula, the remnant of the supernova explosion. A **nebula** is a cloud of gas and dust. Scientists can still see the Crab Nebula expanding nearly 1000 years after the ancient astronomers first reported the explosion.

nebula (plural: nebulae): a cloud of gas and dust in space.

A main sequence star has to have much more mass than the Sun for it to become a supernova. Recent studies suggest that such a supernova would have to be within 25 light-years of Earth for the radiation to have an impact on Earth's atmosphere. Fortunately, no stars within 25 light-years of Earth have enough mass to explode in this way. Unfortunately, there is another type of supernova that could be a threat to life on Earth.

The first supernova known to have been witnessed on Earth was seen in the year 185 C.E. It may have been the brightest object in the sky, aside from the Sun and the Moon. It had an absolute magnitude of −8 when it first occurred. However, this supernova was the result of an exploding white dwarf. This is a different kind of explosion from that of a main sequence star, and one that is much more dangerous.

Astronomer Subrahmanyan Chandrasekhar won a Nobel prize for his investigations on the structure of stars.

Subrahmanyan Chandrasekhar was an Indian-born astronomer who became a U.S. citizen in 1953. In 1983, he won the Nobel prize for his work on the structure of stars. He is best known for his calculation that showed if a star forming a white dwarf has a mass greater than 1.4 times the mass of the Sun, it will explode as a supernova.

As already mentioned, most stars in the universe are found in binary systems. If one of the two stars in a binary system becomes a white dwarf, it may begin to strip the other star of material. Once enough material falls onto the white dwarf so that its mass exceeds an account that Chandrasekhar calculated, a supernova occurs. In this explosion, the star is completely destroyed and matter and energy are ejected into space.

This type of supernova is much more powerful than the one caused by the collapsing core of a supergiant star. If such an explosion occurred within 3000 light-years of Earth, life on Earth would probably be affected.

Supernovas occur about once every 50 years in the Milky Way galaxy. Fortunately, it has probably been hundreds of millions of years since one happened close enough to Earth to be dangerous. In addition, the effects of supernovas are not all bad. Scientists think that a supernova can trigger the formation of new stars from the clouds of dust and gas in space. Most of the matter in stars is hydrogen and helium. Any other elements that are found in the universe were formed within stars and released by stars in events such as supernovas. This means that all of the material other than hydrogen and helium that is found on Earth—including most of what is found in you—was originally made inside a star.

Stop and Think

1. Describe the types of stars you can see in the night sky.

2. Describe the life cycle of the Sun, starting from the original nebula that formed it to its final stages as a red giant.

3. Give reasons why you think supernovas may or may not be more dangerous than collisions.

4. Astronomers theorize that the Milky Way has a supermassive black hole in its center. The Milky Way's black hole is estimated to contain over 4 million times the mass of the Sun. List reasons why or why not the center of the galaxy is a potential danger to Earth.

What's the Point?

Normal stars come in several types, ranging from red stars much smaller than the Sun to giant blue stars much larger than the Sun. Other types of stars include white dwarfs, giants, supergiants, and neutron stars. Most stars will eventually become white dwarfs once the process of fusion stops inside the star. Stars with enough mass can end in a violent explosion called a supernova, leading to the formation of a neutron star or a black hole. Supernovas may pose a threat to Earth, but only if they occur within 3000 light-years of Earth. Because the galaxy is 100,000 light-years across, most supernovas in the galaxy would be too far away to harm Earth.

4.6 Explore

Can Galaxies Collide?

In ancient times most people thought of the universe as the Sun, the Moon, and planets revolving around Earth. The stars were considered attached to a giant celestial sphere that defined the outer edge of the universe. It was not until the 17th century that astronomers began to recognize stars as other suns. The first parallax measurement, which showed that stars are very distant and not part of our solar system, was made in 1834.

At the beginning of the 20th century, scientists recognized that Earth and the Sun are part of the Milky Way galaxy, a vast collection of stars, gas, and dust. Many objects that looked like nebulae had been discovered with telescopes, and these were all thought to be part of the Milky Way galaxy.

Astronomer Henrietta Swan Leavitt developed a way to estimate the distance to clusters of stars, like those on the left, by measuring their brightness.

By 1920, astronomers were sharply divided over whether these nebulae were within the Milky Way galaxy or whether they were separate galaxies. A famous debate between astronomers Harlow Shapley and Heber Curtis in 1920 captured the main ideas of the two points of view. Shapley argued that the Milky Way galaxy was the extent of the universe. Curtis argued that the Milky Way was just one small part of a much larger universe.

The groundwork for settling the debate was laid years earlier by Henrietta Swan Leavitt. Like Annie Jump Cannon, she worked at the Harvard College Observatory. She was studying a variable star in two oddly shaped nebulae called the Magellanic Clouds. She determined a way to estimate the distance to far-off clusters of stars by measuring the changes in brightness of these variable stars. This discovery gave astronomers their first reliable tool for determining the size of the universe.

One of the two nebulae known as the Magellanic Clouds. Leavitt's research involved the study of a variable star within these clouds.

Using Leavitt's variable stars, scientists calculated that the Magellanic Clouds were 150,000 to 200,000 light-years from Earth. In their debate, Shapley argued that this was within the Milky Way galaxy, but Curtis argued that the galaxy was much smaller than that. In 1925, the astronomer Edwin Hubble found evidence that settled the argument for good.

Edwin Hubble did a study of stars in what was then known as the Andromeda Nebula. The nebula is a spectacular spiral galaxy, located in the constellation Andromeda, which is visible to the naked eye. Hubble came across a star that he realized was the same type of variable star that Leavitt had studied. The dimness of the star suggested to Hubble that the nebula was much too far from Earth to be within the Milky Way galaxy.

In fact, the Andromeda galaxy is about 2.5 million light-years from Earth. Andromeda and the Milky Way are part of the *Local Group of Galaxies* that includes at least three dozen members. The Local Group occupies a region of the universe about 10 million light-years in diameter. However, astronomers believe that there are more than 100 billion galaxies in the universe. Since most galaxies contain millions, if not billions, of stars, this means that the universe is vast indeed!

The Andromeda Galaxy is located in the constellation Andromeda. It is so bright, it can be seen without a telescope or binoculars.

Explore

Types of Galaxies

Galaxy 1

Galaxy 2

Galaxy 3

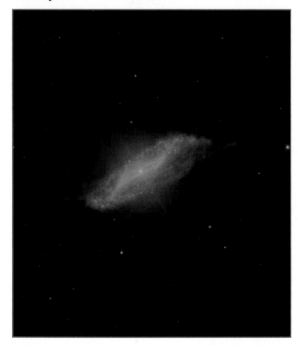

Galaxy 4

Procedure

1. Look at the photographs of galaxies. Identify similarities and differences among the appearances of these galaxies.

2. Using the similarities and differences that you have identified, classify the galaxies using two or more categories.

3. Give a name to each category, and briefly describe the characteristics of galaxies within each category. Your categories should be defined so that each galaxy can be placed in one and only one category.

Communicate

Share Your Results

Choose one person from your group to share your classification of galaxies with the rest of the class. Listen to what the other groups have to say about their classifications. Be respectful of the other groups as they share their results. Ask questions if you do not understand how they came to their results. Note how the categories they chose differ from your categories.

After listening to all of the other groups, meet again with your group. Adjust your categories to get rid of any inconsistency or overlaps in your categories. Revise your categories to be what you think is the best way to classify galaxies.

Stop and Think

Arp 272

1. Describe any categories that were used by most of the groups in the class. Which galaxies were sorted into these categories, and what characteristics do they share?

2. Which galaxies caused groups to have the most varied opinions on how they should be classified? What were the characteristics of those galaxies?

3. Here is an image of an object that was named Arp 272. How would you categorize this object? Give reasons for your classification. If Arp 272 does not fit into your categories, how will you have to revise your categories?

Types of Galaxies

Much like Annie Jump Cannon classifying stars, Edwin Hubble established a classification system for galaxies. His system, with modifications, is still used by astronomers today.

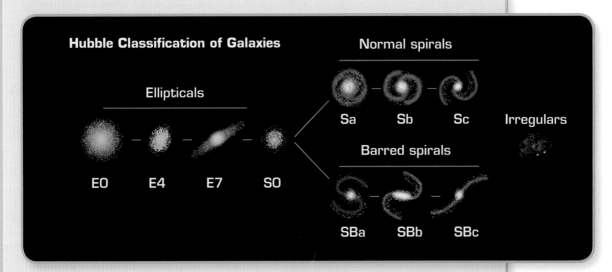

Edwin Hubble developed the standard classification system for galaxies. It is named for him, as is the Hubble Space Telescope.

The main classifications that scientists use to describe galaxies are *elliptical, spiral,* and *barred spiral.* Elliptical galaxies look like a sphere or an elongated sphere of stars that is brightest in the middle. Spiral galaxies are shaped like a spiral with arms extending from the center. They are relatively flat and disc-shaped, with a bulge in the center. Spiral galaxies appear different depending on whether they present a side view or a top-down view. Barred spiral galaxies have a spiral shape, but they also have a long bar shape that passes through the center. The Milky Way galaxy is difficult to classify from the inside, but most scientists think it is a barred spiral galaxy (type SBc).

Galaxies that do not fit into this classification scheme are called *irregular galaxies.* The most likely reason for the odd shape of an irregular galaxy would seem to be that it collided with another galaxy or was affected by the gravity of another galaxy in the past. At least 3% of the galaxies observed so far are irregular galaxies.

Colliding Galaxies

Astronomers can see that some galaxies are in the process of colliding, or have collided in the past. Is there a chance that the Milky Way will collide with another galaxy? To determine the answer to this question, scientists need to study the motions of galaxies. They can do this using the same method used to determine if stars are moving toward Earth. Galaxies, like stars, have redshifts and blueshifts.

Studying Doppler shifts of galaxies has had an unexpected result. Within the Milky Way galaxy, stars are moving in all different directions depending upon their motion around the center of the galaxy. But almost all galaxies are moving away from us. It turns out that the farther away the galaxies are, the faster they are moving. This suggests that the universe is expanding.

Hoag's Object, pictured in the photograph below taken by the Hubble Space Telescope, is a type of irregular galaxy known as a ring galaxy.

Astronomers have several theories about why the universe is expanding. Each comes from a theory about how the universe formed. In one theory, called the Big Bang Theory, all of the matter in the universe was collected in a single point about 14 billion years ago. Then the Big Bang occurred, and all of the matter was flung outward as the universe expanded. The universe is still expanding from that explosion today.

Even though galaxies are moving apart, they can still collide. In fact, there is evidence that many smaller galaxies have been consumed by the Milky Way in the past. Some astronomers believe that one such small galaxy is merging with the Milky Way galaxy now. These small collisions result in the smaller galaxy being torn apart with little effect to the Milky Way. Collisions with galaxies do not seem to have affected Earth.

Astronomers have found many examples of galaxies colliding. The collisions do not necessarily result in many stars colliding with one another. Remember, there is a lot of space between stars. But the collisions can alter the paths of stars in a gravitational tug of war.

The gas inside galaxies is heated as galaxies pass through each other. This can create intense conditions, with lots of radiation. It would be hard to imagine life existing on a planet circling a star in a region like this.

The Andromeda galaxy is one of the few galaxies moving toward Earth. Scientists believe there is a good chance Andromeda will collide with the Milky Way. Other galaxies are either too small or too far way to be a concern. This collision, out of all the intergalactic collisions, may be the one that affects life on Earth. Fortunately, this collision will not happen until more than 2 billion years from now.

Stop and Think

1. Describe how the known scale of the universe has changed from ancient times through now as more and more discoveries about objects in the night sky have been made.

2. List reasons why a collision with another galaxy is or is not a potential danger for Earth in the next 30 years.

Update the *Project Board*

In this section you have learned about the possibility of galaxies colliding with the Milky Way galaxy. Update the *Project Board* with your new knowledge to the *What are we learning?* and *What is our evidence?* columns.

What's the Point?

In the past 100 years, astronomers have discovered that the Milky Way galaxy is one galaxy among billions of galaxies. These galaxies can be classified into spiral, elliptical, barred elliptical, and irregular types. Many galaxies, including the Milky Way, show evidence of past collisions. Because of the vast distances between stars and the immense size of galaxies, the Milky Way can collide with another galaxy without affecting Earth.

4.7 Read

How Is Technology Aiding New Discoveries in Astronomy?

Four hundred years ago, Galileo started looking at the sky with his new and improved telescope. He saw wonders he could not have imagined. He discovered that the markings on the Moon were impact craters. He was the first to see that another planet besides Earth has moons. He showed that Venus was orbiting the Sun and not Earth.

Galileo used a telescope that allowed him to see objects 20 times dimmer than the naked eye can see. Today, telescopes can detect objects that are billions of times dimmer than those Galileo was able to see. This has helped astronomers to learn much more about the characteristics of each planet and the Sun. Their knowledge of what is beyond the solar system also expands every day.

Currently, two important space telescopes are helping to build knowledge of the universe beyond our solar system. One is the Hubble Space Telescope, which was launched into space in 1990. The other is the Kepler Mission, which was launched in 2009. They are both telescopes, but their jobs are very different and the data they collect and send back to Earth are very different.

Case Study 1: The Hubble Space Telescope

The Hubble Space Telescope is actually six separate instruments that can view the universe in many different ways. It was placed in Earth orbit during a space shuttle mission in 1990. It was designed so that astronauts could repair the telescope in space if necessary. Five space shuttle missions between 1993 and 2009 have been launched to repair or increase the capabilities of the Hubble.

The Hubble Space Telescope can do what no telescope on Earth can do—look at stars without having to look through Earth's atmosphere. In *Learning Set 3*, you learned that stars twinkle because the atmosphere distorts and scatters the light from stars. This limits the ability of telescopes on Earth to "see" objects that are very dim, or to view fine details on objects in space. In addition, the atmosphere blocks light at certain wavelengths from reaching the ground.

Astronauts repair the massive Hubble Space Telescope.

The Hubble Space Telescope gets around these problems by observing objects from above Earth's atmosphere. It orbits Earth at more than 550 km (342 mi) above Earth's surface, which is well outside the atmosphere. For comparison, a commercial airplane flies up to 9 km (5.6 mi) above Earth's surface. Astronomers are able to collect data and guide the telescope by remote control. The telescope sends data and images back to Earth using a radio antenna and other communication satellites.

The Hubble Space Telescope has been a success even outside of science because of the many beautiful images it has taken over the past 20 years. Many of the images you have seen in this *Learning Set* have come from the Hubble Space Telescope. Hubble provided much of the data showing that most galaxies have a super-massive black hole in their centers. It has sent back images of galaxies that appear to be colliding and galaxies that appear to be forming. It has sent back images of objects as far away as 13 billion light-years from Earth. Because it took the light 13 billion years to travel from these objects to the telescope, you could also say that the Hubble has looked back 13 billion years into the past.

Eris was first identified in 2005 and originally billed as the tenth planet because it was larger than Pluto. Disagreement about how to classify Eris was resolved by the International Astronomical Union in 2006. They decided to define both Pluto and Eris as dwarf planets and reduce the number of planets to eight.

Hubble's discoveries are not limited to objects outside the solar system. Hubble helped astronomers identify the precise orbit of the Shoemaker-Levy 9 comet before it collided with Jupiter. It has been used to study the dwarf planets Eris and Pluto, which so far have not been visited by a probe. It has also surveyed other dim objects in the solar system's Kuiper Belt. These objects orbit the Sun from near Neptune to about twice Neptune's distance from the Sun. Over 1000 such objects have been identified, many with the aid of the Hubble Space Telescope.

This elliptical galaxy is ejecting a stream of hot material, probably resulting from energy released by matter falling into a super-massive black hole at the galaxy's center.

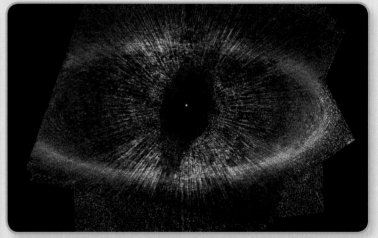

Artist's conception of the dwarf planet Eris (front).

Some of Hubble's most exciting recent work focuses on finding planetary systems around other stars. Hubble has also been able to detect disks of debris, such as this one, around other stars.

Observe

NASA Video: A Hubble Space Telescope Discovery

You will be watching a video about a recent Hubble Space Telescope discovery. The discovery took place when astronomers analyzed an image of the star Fomalhaut, which is 25 light-years from Earth. Fomalhaut, thanks to the Hubble Space Telescope, is one of the stars known to have a disk of debris around it. The video shows a Hubble image that marks the first time that astronomers have seen a certain type of object. Watch the video, taking notes as necessary. Be prepared to answer the questions below after the video is over.

Reflect

1. What was the discovery mentioned in the video? What is the significance of the discovery?

2. How do you think the Hubble Space Telescope helped make the discovery possible?

3. What further information do you think astronomers should try to find out about this new discovery?

Case Study 2: The Kepler Mission

The Kepler Mission is a telescope that will search for Earth-like planets that orbit other stars. It was launched in 2009 and will search nearby stars for planets until at least 2012. It will collect data on the planetary systems of other stars, and explore the structure and variety of the systems. The Kepler Mission will focus on the same 100,000 stars for its entire mission, measuring changes in their brightness every 30 minutes.

The Kepler Mission is named after Johannes Kepler, a German astronomer who worked in the early 17th century. He was the first to accurately describe the orbits of the planets around the Sun, summarizing his findings in what are now called Kepler's laws of planetary motion.

The method that the Kepler Mission will use is to look for planets that pass in front of stars. When a planet that is orbiting a star passes directly between the telescope and a star, a small portion of the light

from the star is blocked. The star temporarily appears to be dimmer than it actually is. If enough of these *transits* are witnessed, then astronomers can confirm that a planet-sized object is passing in front of the star. They can also make estimates of the planet's size and its orbit.

Before the Kepler Mission began, astronomers had found over 300 planets around other stars. However, most of those planets were very large gas giants that orbit very close to their star. These findings do not mean that most planets are large and close to stars, but that these types of planets are the easiest to detect. Larger planets can block more light than smaller planets during a transit. And planets that are close to stars also travel past the star more often.

Most planets identified before the Kepler Mission were gas giants orbiting very close to their stars.

The Kepler Mission telescope.

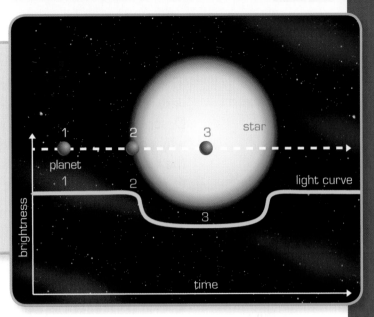

The Kepler Mission is designed so that it will have the necessary accuracy to find planets about the size of Earth orbiting at distances that allow water to be in a liquid state. These planets are called Earth-like planets. To have this accuracy, Kepler has to be able to collect light from all the stars it is pointing at for a long time, and it has to have the ability to detect very slight changes in a star's light.

Observe

NASA Video: The Kepler Misson

You will watch a video that describes the Kepler Mission in more detail. Read the questions below before watching the video. Then, when you watch the video, take notes to prepare to answer the questions. Also, record questions about anything you find confusing or that you want to know more about.

By studying the variations in brightness of stars, or transits, astronomers can learn about the sizes and orbits of objects in space. Not to scale.

Reflect

1. What is an Earth-like planet? Do you think the Kepler mission will find more Earth-like planets or more Jupiter-sized planets?

2. What is the "Goldilocks Zone?" Why is this zone important to finding Earth-like planets?

3. What characteristics of a planet make it habitable? What would make it uninhabitable?

4. What advantages are there to focus on such a small area of space? What are the disadvantages?

5. A pixel is the smallest element of an image. A digital camera works by recording the amount of light that falls on an array of pixels. The pattern of brighter and darker pixels then becomes the image that you see on a display screen. Why is it important that the camera used in the Kepler Mission contains 95 million megapixels?

6. In your opinion, how likely is the mission to be successful?

Conference

The purposes of the Hubble Space Telescope and the Kepler Mission are very different. Both will probably end between the years 2012 and 2014. Describe which program you think is more important and give some reasons why you think this. Use evidence from the readings in this section and from the videos you watched. Discuss your opinions with your group. Remember to respect opinions that are different from yours.

Together with your group members, come up with your ideal space mission. Assume that the mission will be unmanned, and the probe or object launched will not leave the solar system. Develop a list of goals for a mission and the outline of a plan that would achieve those goals.

Communicate

Share Your Plan

Every group will now give a presentation that describes their ideal space mission. The presentation should include a poster that lists the goals of the mission, including the scientific questions that the mission will attempt to answer. During each group's presentations, listen closely to their ideas. Offer suggestions that may make the mission more exciting, or ideas that may help the mission be more successful.

What's the Point?

The Hubble Space Telescope, the Kepler Mission, and other telescopes are all looking out into space collecting information. Each astronomical activity has scientists who review the data that is collected from space. When enough data have been collected, the astronomers interpret the data and may come to new and more specific understandings of the universe and how different parts of it interact. Each of these programs has a mission, whether broad as for the Hubble, or specific as for the Kepler Mission. All are trying to gather knowledge of how our universe works.

Learning Set 4

Back to the Big Question

How can you know if objects in space will collide?

You have considered objects within the solar system colliding with other space objects within the solar system. You now know enough about the rest of the Milky Way galaxy and other galaxies to consider the possibility of objects from outside of our solar system colliding with a solar-system object. Add what you know about these types of collisions to your *Big Question* page.

Revise Your Explanation

Now, you will revise your explanation of how you know if two space objects will collide. You have learned a lot since you last revised your explanation, so you will probably need to make several changes. Use a new *Create Your Explanation* page for your revised explanation. Remember that a good explanation has several parts to it.

Start by revising the claim your group agreed upon at the end of *Learning Set 3*. You will need to revise it to include what you now know about space objects outside of our solar system. Then, refine the evidence and science knowledge to support the new parts of your claim.

Develop an explanation statement that combines your claim, evidence, and science knowledge. This should state why you need all the different kinds of data you mention in your claim to predict if two space objects will collide.

Make sure the explanation is accurate and complete. Use what you now know about the motion of stars and other objects in the Milky Way galaxy to check the accuracy of your explanation statement. You may also consider what you learned about types of stars, how stars can change, and the different types of galaxies.

Communicate

Share Your Explanation

Share with the rest of the class your group's explanation of how you can know if objects in space will collide. As you are listening to the explanations of others, look for anything they have included that you might have left out. With the class, agree on a claim and an explanation.

Reflect

With your group, answer the following questions

1. How trustworthy and complete do you think your explanation is?

2. What else do you need to investigate and learn about the solar system to improve your

Update the *Project Board*

The *What are we learning?* column on the *Project Board* helps you pull together everything you have learned. Add to this column any science knowledge you have been using that is not already in that column. Remember to include supporting evidence in the *What is our evidence?* column.

How can you know if objects in space will collide?				
What do we think we know?	What do we need to investigate?	What are we learning?	What is our evidence?	What does it mean for the challenge or question?

The last column, *What does it mean for the challenge or question?* is the place to write down how learning about the locations and movements of the solar-system objects, stars, and galaxies can help you answer the *Big Question: How can you know if objects in space will collide?*

Answer the Big Question

How Can You Know if Objects in Space Will Collide?

Now you will have the opportunity to pull all of your learning together. In this Unit, you have learned about many different objects in space. You are now going to write a report for a movie producer describing the collision between two space objects, and explaining why the collision is realistic for use in a movie. The report will have three parts. *Part 1* will present the possible collision you suggest. *Part 2* will explain why this is a realistic suggestion. *Part 3* should convince the movie producer that this movie will be exciting and can be a hit. To do this, you will need to describe how the collision would look to a character in the movie or to a person in the audience.

Prepare to Write Your Report

Remember that the producer is counting on you, the science consultant, to come up with an idea for a possible collision that will make the movie realistic. The report has several parts.

Part 1: Propose a possible collision between space objects to be used in the movie. It should be realistic and affect Earth, the Sun, or the Moon.

Part 2: Construct a claim and explanation of why the collision you chose is realistic and would affect Earth, the Sun, and the Moon.

Part 3: Convince the producer that the collision you chose is scientifically accurate. To do this, develop an explanation statement that brings together your claim, evidence, and science knowledge. It should state why you need all the different kinds of data you mention in your claim to predict if two space objects will collide.

Choose a Collision

Each member in your group should propose one idea for a collision that could be used in a movie. Remember that you will need to convince a movie producer that your idea is realistic and dramatic. Make suggestions to improve everyone else's proposals and listen carefully to the ideas the rest of the group has about your proposal.

After everyone's proposal has been considered, the group will work together to reach agreement on which collision will be used for your report. Decide together which idea is most realistic and dramatic or develop a new idea based on group members' proposals. Record the details of this collision on a poster. Make sure to include relevant details for each object: location, mass, path or orbit, speed, direction of motion, the effects of gravity, and the effects of other nearby objects.

Revise Your Explanation

You must now develop a final claim and explanation that tells what data and methods scientist use to predict if two space objects will collide. You will need to use those types of data to support your collision choice. Begin by developing a claim that states what makes your collision realistic. You will use this explanation to answer the Big Question and help you answer your report.

Make a list of factors that should be considered, such as:

- the locations of the objects

- the mass of each object

- the paths or orbits of the objects

- the speed of each object and the direction of motion when the collision occurs

- the effects of gravity, perhaps from nearby massive objects

Communicate

Use the feedback from the class when developing your final explanation. Think about anything other class member thought you might have left out or could make clearer.

Write Your Report

Movies that detail collisions and near collisions with Earth have been popular for many years. The crashing of rocks and scenes of destruction are violent and terrifying. The advanced techniques in special effects make the images seem real. But often, these movies are not realistic and all. Your job as the movie's science consultant is to convince a movie producer that the collision you propose can be used to make a movie that is scientifically accurate and also a popular success.

Part 1: Proposal of a Collision for a Movie Script

You have already proposed a collision between two objects in space. Your group chose this collision after considering several others. Now is your chance to incorporate any feedback from the class presentation that your group just made. Make sure that Part 1, including any graphics, fits on one page.

Part 2: Explanation of Why the Collision is Realistic

Producers like getting an executive summary; it can be read quickly, and they can make a fast decision. Keep in mind that "bulleted" lists can be very useful in this kind of report.

The "bullets" (• small, filled-in circles) make each new and important idea easy to identify.

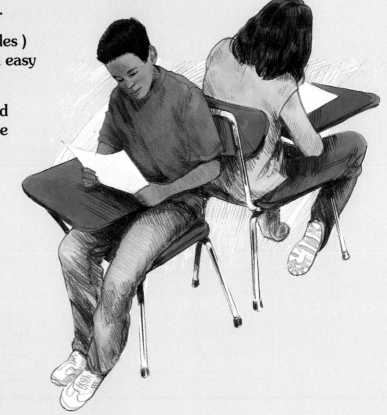

Your task is to revise your claim and explanation so that it fits on a single page and uses bulleted lists.

Make sure you include the four parts of an explanation:

- your claim

- your evidence

- your science knowledge

- your explanation statement

Part 3: Description of How the Collision Will Appear On Screen

Throughout this Unit you have filled out a *Big Question* page that lists the different types of objects in the universe, evidence you have gathered about past collisions with Earth or among these objects, future risks of collisions, and what you think will happen if such a collision occurs. The page has helped you to organize your thinking for this Unit. The last column of this page will be helpful as you write *Part 3* of the report.

To accurately describe the collision, you may want to consider what you have learned about light, telescopes, and electromagnetic radiation. These would be important to consider when you describe how the collision might appear to a character in the movie or to a person watching the movie.

You also will consider the correct scale for the collision objects. The scale below may help you check that your descriptions of sizes are accurate. Keep in mind what you learned about your distance from an object and how this affects how large the object appears.

The Scale of the Universe	
Object	**Approximate Size/Distance**
Largest meteorite found on Earth: Hoba, in Namibia (diameter)	3 m
Full-size school bus (length)	11.5 m
Small Asteroid (diameter)	1 km
Ten regulation football fields (length end to end)	1.1 km
Halley's Comet (diameter)	16 km
Neutron star at center of Crab Nebula (diameter)	20 km
Large Asteroid (diameter)	200 km
Pluto (dwarf planet) (diameter)	2300 km
The Moon (diameter)	3500 km
Mercury (smallest planet) (diameter)	4900 km
Earth (diameter)	12,800 km
Sirius B (white dwarf star) (diameter)	22,000 km
Jupiter (largest planet) (diameter)	143,000 km
Sun (diameter)	1,390,000 km
Betelgeuse (red giant star) (diameter)	820 million km

Pictured is the Hoba meteorite *that landed in what is now the African country of Namibia. It has never been moved from where it fell -- an estimated 80,000 years ago -- perhaps because its main mass is over 60 tons. It is the largest-known meteorite on Earth.*

Betelgeuse, *the yellow circle in the upper left of the picture, is a red supergiant and one of the largest and brightest stars known. It is located approximately 640 light-years away from Earth, and is probably only a few million years old.*

Communicate

Give Your Report

After you complete your report, you will hand it in to your teacher. Then you will imagine that your report has gotten the attention of a movie producer who has asked you to "pitch" the movie idea.

Your teacher will take the role of the movie producer. You will give a short pitch that emphasizes the important points in your report. You should be prepared to answer questions about what you wrote.

After everyone has given their reports, you will have heard many different ideas about what colliding space objects would look like in a movie. Discuss what you have learned from the experience and what you enjoyed the most. Also discuss things that you would like to learn more about. Here are a few questions that you can use to organize the discussion:

1. What evidence from the Unit was used most often to support the idea that collisions will or will not occur?

2. Which movie idea seemed the most popular? What made it popular?

English & Spanish Glossary

A

absolute magnitude The brightness a star would be relative to other stars if all were viewed from the same distance (about 2 million astronomical units).

magnitud absoluta El brillo de una estrella será relativo a otras estrellas si todas fueran vistas desde la misma distancia (alrededor de 2 millones de unidades astronómicas).

apparent magnitude The brightness of a star relative to other stars as seen from Earth.

magnitud aparente El brillo de una estrella relativo a otras estrellas visto desde la Tierra.

asteroid belt A region of the solar system between Mars and Jupiter in which most asteroids are located.

cinturón de asteroides Una región del sistema solar entre Marte y Júpiter, donde están localizados la mayoría de los asteroides.

asteroid A rock or metallic solar-system body that revolves around the Sun, between 10 m (33 ft) and about 500 km (310 mi) in diameter.

asteroide Una roca o un cuerpo metálico del sistema solar que da vueltas alrededor del Sol, con un diámetro que fluctúa entre 10 metros (33 pies) y alrededor de 500 kilómetros (310 millas).

astrogeology The study of the rocks, minerals, and surface features of moons and other planets, applying knowledge of Earth's geology.

astrogeología El estudio de las rocas, minerales, y las características de la superficie de las lunas y otros planetas, aplicando el conocimiento de la geología terrestre.

astronomer A scientist who studies space and objects in space.

astrónomo Un científico que estudia el espacio y los objetos en el espacio.

astronomical unit (AU) A measure of distance based on Earth's orbit. 1 AU is equal to the average distance of Earth from the Sun, about 150 million kilometers.

unidad astronómica (UA) Una medida de la distancia basado en la órbita terrestre. 1 UA es igual a la distancia promedio de la Tierra al Sol, alrededor de 150 millones de kilómetros.

axis A line through the center of a body, around which the body rotates or spins; Earth's imaginary axis passes through the North Pole and the South Pole.

eje Una línea a través del centro de un cuerpo, alrededor del cual el cuerpo rota o gira; el eje imaginario de la Tierra pasa a través de los Polos Norte y Sur.

B

biased sample A sample that does not accurately represent the group from which it was drawn.

muestra sesgada Una muestra que no representa con exactitud el grupo del cual fue extraída.

black hole A body with mass so concentrated that light cannot escape its gravitational pull.

agujero negro Un cuerpo con masa tan concentrada que la luz no puede escapar su halón gravitacional.

blueshift A shift in light toward the blue end of a spectrum, which occurs when the source of light is moving toward the observer.

corrimiento al azul Un desplazamiento de la luz hacia el extremo azul del espectro, el cual ocurre cuando la fuente de luz se mueve en dirección del observador.

C

coma The cloud of gas and dust that forms around a comet as parts of the comet vaporize.

cabellera La nube de gas y polvo que se forma alrededor de un cometa mientras partes del cometa se vaporiza.

comet A small, icy solar-system body that revolves around the Sun and forms a tail as it gets closer to the Sun.

cometa Un cuerpo del sistema solar helado y pequeño que da vueltas alrededor del Sol y forma una cola mientras se acerca al Sol.

control variable In an experiment, a variable that is kept constant (not changed).

variable controlada En un experimento, una variable que se mantiene constante (no cambia).

corona Outer portion of the Sun's atmosphere, consisting of superheated gases.

corona Porción externa de la atmósfera solar, que consiste de gases extremadamente calientes.

crater A rounded depression in the surface of a planet, moon, or solid body.

cráter Una depresión redonda en la superficie de un planeta, luna o un cuerpo sólido.

D

day The amount of time it takes a body to spin once on its axis.

día La cantidad de tiempo que le toma a un cuerpo girar una vez sobre su eje.

degree A unit of measure for angles. A complete circle is 360° (360 degrees).

grado Una unidad de medida para los ángulos. Un círculo completo mide 360° (360 grados).

dependent (responding) variable A factor that is affected by changes in the independent (manipulated) variable.

variable dependiente (de respuesta) Un factor que se afecta por los cambios en la variable independiente (manipulada).

Doppler shift The observed change that an object's motion causes in wavelengths.

desplazamiento Doppler El cambio observado que el movimiento de un objeto causa en las longitudes de onda.

dwarf planet A round solar-system body that is smaller than a planet.

planeta enano Un cuerpo redondo del sistema solar que es más pequeño que un planeta.

E

eccentricity A measurement used to describe the shape of an ellipse.

excentricidad Una medida utilizada para describir la forma de una elipse.

eclipse The blocking of light from one object in space by another object in space, as seen from a particular location.

eclipse El bloqueo de luz de un objeto en el espacio por otro objeto en el espacio, visto desde un lugar determinado.

ellipse A shape that is a squashed or flattened circle. The sum of the distances from a point on the ellipse to each of the two foci is the same for every point on the ellipse.

elipse Una forma que es un círculo aplastado o achatado. La suma de las distancias de un punto en la elipse a cada uno de los dos focos es igual para cada punto en la elipse.

erosion A process in which rocks on Earth's surface are worn down and carried away by wind or water.

erosión Un proceso en el cual las rocas de la superficie terrestre son desgastadas y arrastradas por el viento o el agua.

F

focus (plural: foci) One of two fixed points that determine the shape of an ellipse.

foco (plural: focos) Uno de dos puntos fijos que determinan la forma de una elipse.

fusion reaction A change in which one or more low-mass elements produces a higher-mass element, with a release of enormous amounts of energy.

reacción de fusión Un cambio en el cual uno o más elementos con poca masa producen un elemento con mayor masa, con una liberación de enormes cantidades de energía.

G

galaxy A system of stars, gas, and dust held together by gravity.

galaxia Un sistema de estrellas, gas, y polvo que se mantienen unidas por la gravedad.

geocentric model Model of the solar system in which Earth is at the center.

modelo geocéntrico Modelo del sistema solar en el cual la Tierra se encuentra en el centro.

geologist A person who is trained in and works in any of the geologic sciences.

geólogo Una persona entrenada en y que trabaja en cualquiera de las ciencias geológicas.

geology (geologic) The study of the planet Earth, the materials of which it is made, the processes that act on these materials, the products formed, and the history of the planet and all its forms since its origin.

geología (geológico) El estudio del planeta Tierra, los materiales que lo componen, los procesos que actúan sobre esos materiales, los productos que se forman, y la historia del planeta y todas sus formas desde su origen.

giant star A star that is larger than a main sequence star of the same color.

estrella gigante Una estrella que es más grande que una estrella de una secuencia principal del mismo color.

gnomon The object on a sundial blocking direct light from the Sun and casting a shadow.

nomon Un objeto sobre un reloj solar que bloquea la luz directa del Sol y forma una sombra.

gravity The force of attraction between two objects due to their mass; the greater the mass in each object, the stronger the attraction; the more distance between the objects, the weaker the attraction.

gravedad La fuerza de atracción entre dos objetos debido a sus masas; a mayor masa en cada objeto, mayor es la atracción; mientras más distancia entre los objetos, menor es la atracción.

H

heliocentric model Model of the solar system in which the Sun is at the center.

modelo heliocéntrico Modelo del sistema solar en el cual el Sol se encuentra en el centro.

high tide The time, for a certain location, when the tide is at its highest point.

marea alta El momento para un lugar determinado cuando la marea se encuentra en su punto más alto.

horizon The line at which the sky and Earth appear to meet.

horizonte La línea donde el cielo y la Tierra parecen unirse.

hypothesis A prediction of what will happen to a dependent (responding) variable when a change is made to the independent (manipulated) variable while other variables are held constant. A hypothesis is not a guess; it is always based on what you know.

hipótesis Una predicción de lo que le sucederá a una variable dependiente (de respuesta) cuando se cambia la variable independiente (manipulada) mientras otras variables se mantienen constantes. Una hipótesis no es una conjetura; siempre se basa en lo que sabes.

I

impact crater A crater formed when an object strikes a planet, moon, or solid body.

cráter de impacto Un cráter formado cuando un objeto choca con un planeta, luna, o un cuerpo sólido.

independent (manipulated) variable A factor that is changed or manipulated in an experiment.

variable independiente (manipulada) Un factor que es cambiado o manipulado en un experimento.

L

light year A unit of distance equal to the distance light travels in a year, about 9,460,000,000,000 km.

año luz Una unidad de distancia igual a la distancia que viaja la luz en un año, alrededor de 9,460,000,000,000 kilómetros.

low tide The time, for a certain location, when the tide is at its lowest point.

marea baja El momento para un lugar determinado cuando la marea se encuentra en su punto más bajo.

lunar eclipse When the Moon passes through Earth's shadow so that some or all of the Moon can only be seen by reflected light from Earth.

eclipse lunar Cuando la Luna pasa a través de la sombra de la Tierra de manera que una parte o toda la Luna puede verse sólo reflejada por la luz de la Tierra.

lunar horizon the line at which the sky and Moon appear to meet.

horizonte lunar la línea donde el cielo y la Luna parecen unirse.

M

main sequence star A typical star, usually with a diameter between one-eighth and 10 times the Sun's diameter.

estrella de secuencia principal Una estrella típica, usualmente con un diámetro entre un octavo y 10 veces el diámetro del Sol.

meteor An object that enters Earth's atmosphere with such speed that it glows.

meteoro Un objeto que entra la atmósfera terrestre a tal velocidad que brilla.

meteorite An object that enters Earth's atmosphere at high speed and reaches the ground without burning up.

meteorito Un objeto que entra la atmósfera terrestre a altas velocidades y llega al suelo sin quemarse.

meteoroid A small solar-system body that has the potential to become a meteor.

meteoroide Un cuerpo pequeño del sistema solar que tiene el potencial de convertirse en un meteoro.

N

nanometer (nm) One billionth of a meter.

nanómetro (nm) Una billonésima parte de un metro.

Near-Earth Objects (NEOs) Asteroids and comets that cross the orbit of Earth.

Objetos Cercanos a la Tierra (NEO por sus siglas en inglés) Asteroides y cometas que cruzan la órbita terrestre.

nebula (plural: nebulae) A cloud of gas and dust in space.

nebulosa (plural: nebulosas) Una nube de gas y polvo en el espacio.

neutron star A supernova remnant with more mass than the Sun, packed into a sphere about 20 kilometers in diameter.

estrella de neutrones El residuo de una supernova con masa mayor que el Sol compactado en una esfera con un diámetro de alrededor de 20 kilómetros.

O

orbit The path that a solar-system object takes in revolving around another solar-system object.

órbita La ruta que toma un objeto del sistema solar al dar vueltas alrededor de otro objeto del sistema solar.

orrery A mechanical model of our solar system used to show the relative positions and movements of the planets.

planetario Un modelo mecánico de nuestro sistema solar usado para mostrar las posiciones relativas y los movimientos de los planetas.

P

parallax The observable change in an object's apparent position relative to a distant background when observed from two locations that are the same distance from the object.

paralaje El cambio observable en la posición aparente de un objeto relativo a un trasfondo distante cuando se observa desde dos lugares que se encuentran a la misma distancia del objeto.

partial eclipse The blocking of a portion of light from one object in space by another object in space, as seen from a particular location.

eclipse parcial El bloqueo de una porción de la luz de un objeto en el espacio por otro objeto en el espacio, visto desde un lugar determinado.

penumbra The lighter, outer shadow cast by an object; the penumbra surrounds the umbra.

penumbra La sombra iluminada, externa emitida por un objeto, la penumbra rodea la sombra.

period (of an orbiting object) The time it takes an object to complete one revolution around another space object.

período (de un objeto en órbita) El tiempo que le toma a un objeto completar una vuelta alrededor de otro objeto espacial.

phase of the moon The illuminated part of the Moon visible from Earth at a given time.

fase lunar La parte iluminada de la Luna visible desde la Tierra en un momento dado.

probe A remotely controlled spacecraft with data collection equipment used to gather data about objects in space.

sonda Una aeronave controlada a distancia con equipo para recolectar datos utilizada para recopilar información sobre los objetos en el espacio.

pupil The circular opening in the center of the eye that controls the amount of light that enters the eye.

pupila La apertura redonda en el centro del ojo que controla la cantidad de luz que entra al ojo.

R

redshift The shift in light toward the red end of a spectrum, which occurs when the source of light is moving away from the observer.

corrimiento al rojo El desplazamiento de la luz hacia el extremo rojo de un espectro, el cual ocurre cuando la fuente de luz se aleja del observador.

reflected Bounced back off a surface.

reflejado Rebotar de una superficie.

reflection Bouncing back of light from a surface.

reflexión El rebote de luz de una superficie.

representative Describing a subset that has characteristics that closely match the characteristics of the whole set.

representativo La descripción de un subconjunto que tiene características que corresponden estrechamente con las características del conjunto completo.

retrograde motion Motion of an outer planet in which the planet appears to reverse direction as seen from Earth.

movimiento retrógrado Movimiento de un planeta exterior en el cual el planeta aparenta cambiar de dirección al ser visto desde la Tierra.

revolve To move in a curved path determined by the gravity of another object.

girar Moverse en un trayecto curvo determinado por la gravedad de otro objeto.

S

sample A subset of a set for which data are collected.

muestra Un subconjunto de un conjunto para el cual se recopilan datos.

satellite A smaller object that is in orbit around a larger object.

satélite Un objeto más pequeño que se encuentra en una órbita alrededor de otro objeto más grande.

satellite image An image taken by an artificial object placed in orbit around Earth.

imagen de satélite Una imagen tomada por un objeto artificial colocado en órbita alrededor de la Tierra.

scale The ratio of the size of a drawing of an object or place to the size of the actual object or place.

escala La proporción del tamaño de un dibujo de un objeto o un lugar al tamaño actual del objeto o lugar.

scale factor A ratio used to convert the actual size of an object to the size in a model of that object.

factor de escala Una proporción usada para convertir los tamaños reales de un objeto a tamaños en un modelo de ese objeto.

scale model A representation of an object that is related to the actual dimensions of the object by a fixed ratio.

modelo de escala Una representación de un objeto que está relacionada a las dimensiones reales del objeto por una proporción fija.

solar eclipse When the Moon passes between the Sun and Earth, so that light from the Sun is partially or totally blocked.

eclipse solar Cuando la Luna pasa entre el Sol y la Tierra, de manera que la luz del Sol es bloqueada parcial o totalmente.

solar system The Sun and the planets, comets, asteroids, and all the other bodies that revolve around it.

sistema solar El Sol y los planetas, cometas, asteroides, y todos los otros cuerpos que dan vueltas a su alrededor.

spectroscope An instrument used to study the spectrum of a light source.

espectroscopio Un instrumento utilizado para estudiar el espectro de una fuente de luz.

spectrum (plural: spectra) The band of colors formed when white light is separated into its components.

espectro (plural: espectros) La banda de colores formada cuando la luz blanca es separada en sus componentes.

sundial A device that measures time using shadows cast by an object that blocks the Sun's light.

reloj de sol Un artefacto que mide el tiempo usando las sombras formadas por un objeto que bloquea la luz solar.

supergiant star A star that is hundreds or thousands times larger than a main sequence star of the same color.

estrella supergigante Una estrella que es cientos o miles de veces más grande que una estrella de secuencia principal del mismo color.

supernova An explosion of a white dwarf or a star several times the mass of the Sun.

supernova Una explosión de una enana blanca o una estrella varias veces la masa del Sol.

T

theory A model or set of ideas used to explain why things occur or have occurred; a theory is based on comprehensive experimental evidence but is subject to change should new evidence be presented that contradicts the theory.

teoría Un modelo o conjunto de ideas utilizados para explicar por qué las cosas ocurren o han ocurrido; una teoría se basa en evidencia experimental extensa, pero está sujeta a cambio si se presenta evidencia nueva que contradiga la teoría.

tide The rise and fall of the surface level of a body of water due to the Moon's and the Sun's gravitational pull.

marea La subida y bajada del nivel de la superficie de un cuerpo de agua debido al halón gravitacional de la Luna y el Sol.

total eclipse The complete blocking of light from one object in space by another object in space, as seen from a particular location.

eclipse total El bloqueo de la luz de un objeto en el espacio por otro objeto en el espacio, visto desde un lugar determinado.

U

umbra The dark, inner shadow cast by an object.

umbra La sombra interior oscura formada por un objeto.

universe Everything that exists, including all objects in space.

universo Todo lo que existe, incluyendo todos los objetos en el espacio.

V

variable A quantity whose value may change (vary) over the course of an experiment.

variable Una cantidad cuyo valor puede cambiar (variar) a través del curso de un experimento.

W

weathering A process in which rocks on Earth's surface are broken down into smaller parts.

desgaste Un proceso en el cual las rocas de la superficie terrestre son desintegradas en partes más pequeñas.

white dwarf A star about the same size as Earth and with about the same mass as the Sun.

enana blanca Una estrella que tiene aproximadamente el mismo tamaño de la Tierra y aproximadamente la misma masa del Sol.

Y

year The time it takes for a solar-system object to make one complete revolution around the Sun.

año El tiempo que le toma a un objeto del sistema solar dar una vuelta completa alrededor del Sol.

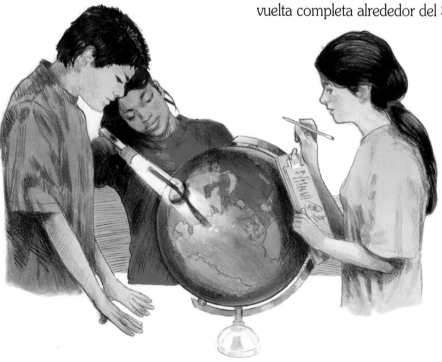

Index

IT'S ABOUT TIME®
YOUR PARTNER IN STEM EDUCATION

333 North Bedford Road, Mount Kisco, NY 10549
Phone (914) 273-2233 Fax (914) 206-6444
www.IAT.com

Publishing Team

Co-Presidents
Tom Laster and Laurie Kreindler

Director of Product Development
Barbara Zahm, Ph.D.

Creative Director
John Nordland

Managing Editor
Maureen Grassi

Production/Studio Manager
Robert Schwalb

Project Development Editor
Ruta Demery

Layout
Sean Campbell

Project Manager
Sarah V. Gruber

Illustration
Thomas Bunk
Dennis Falcon

**Associate Editor,
Student Edition**
Nomi Schwartz

**Technical Art/
Photo Research**
Sean Campbell

**Assistant Editor,
Teacher's Planning Guide**
Kelly Crowley

Jorge Cifuentes

Melissa Ericksen

Equipment Kit Developer
Dana Turner
Henry J. Garcia

Doreen Flaherty

Fredy Fleck

Michael Hortens

Marie Killoran

Louise Landry

Brittany Peters

Cora Roman

MaryBeth Schulze

Jason Skinner

Krystal Stephens

Pre-press
Rich Ciotti